REWARD

Intermediate

Practice Book

Diana Pye
Simon Greenall

Heinemann

1 | *Could I ask you something?*

VOCABULARY AND SOUNDS

1 Say these words aloud. Underline the stressed syllables.

<u>ab</u>road   address   aloud   answer   children
complete   explain   fluent   foreign   journey
married   mistake   pronounce   repeat   single

🔊 Listen and check. Which words are stressed on the first syllable? Which words are stressed on the second syllable?

2 Choose words from activity 1 that can go in the *Classroom* and *Private life* columns of this table.

Classroom	Private life	Work
aloud	*address*	
_____	_____	_____
_____	_____	_____
_____	_____	_____
_____	_____	_____
_____	_____	_____

Write six words in the column headed *Work*.

3 Complete the questions with words from the list in activity 1.

1 Are you _____? No, I'm single.
2 Do you have any _____?
   Yes, I have two sons.
3 Are you _____ in any other
   _____ languages?
4 Do you often travel _____?
   Very rarely. I occasionally visit the branch office in Italy, but that's about all.
5 Do you have a long _____ to work every day?
   Not at all. It only takes me about fifteen minutes by car.

🔊 Listen and check. Notice the rising intonation in questions.

Say the questions aloud.

FUNCTIONS

1 Look at the common classroom situations 1 to 8 below. Which of the questions a to h could you ask the teacher in each situation? Put the correct letters in the boxes.

1 You don't know how to write a word. ☐
2 You don't know the English word for something. ☐
3 You don't understand the meaning of a word. ☐
4 You didn't hear what someone said because they spoke too fast. ☐
5 You didn't understand what someone said. ☐
6 You don't understand a grammatical point. ☐
7 You have finished an activity and don't know what to do. ☐
8 You don't know what page an exercise is on. ☐

a What do I do next?
b Could you explain that again, please?
c Could you repeat that, please?
d What page are we on?
e What's the English for 'bon appétit'?
f How do you spell 'answer'?
g Could you speak more slowly, please?
h What does 'function' mean?

2 Say the questions in activity 1 aloud. Underline the stressed words.

🔊 Listen and repeat.

GRAMMAR

1 Complete the questions with the correct form of *be*, *do* or *have*.

1 <u>*Do*</u> you have any brothers or sisters?

2 _____ you born in Britain?

3 _____ you have a big breakfast this morning?

4 _____ you enjoy learning English?

5 _____ you learn any other languages at school?

6 _____ you ever been to the USA?

7 _____ you interested in music?

8 _____ you know any of the other students before you started the English course?

2 Write answers to the questions in activity 1.

1 _____

2 _____

3 _____

4 _____

5 _____

6 _____

7 _____

8 _____

3 Complete the questions with suitable question words: *what*, *who*, *where*, *when*, *why*, *how*.

1 <u>*When*</u> do you leave home in the morning to come to your English class?

2 _____ do you travel to work or to your class?

3 _____ are you studying English and not another language?

4 _____ is the person you most admire?

5 _____ do you like to do in your spare time?

6 _____ did you go for your holiday last year?

7 _____ did you last go to a restaurant?

8 _____ is your favourite writer?

4 Write answers to the questions in activity 3.

1 _____

2 _____

3 _____

4 _____

5 _____

6 _____

7 _____

8 _____

LISTENING

1 Dan is an Australian who lives in Britain. Look at the photo and write six questions you could ask him. Use the words below.

a when When *did you come to live in Britain?*

b job What _____

_____

c dangerous Is _____

_____

d miss most/Australia What _____

_____

e go back/Australia Have _____

_____

f come/Britain Why _____

_____

g travel Do _____

_____

2 🔊 Listen to Dan talking about himself. In which order does he answer the questions in activity 1? Write the letter of the question in the correct box.

1 ☐   2 ☐   3 ☐   4 ☐   5 ☐

6 ☐   7 ☐

3 🔊 Find out more about Dan. Listen and tick (✓) the questions Dan answers.

1 Are you married? ☐

2 Do you enjoy your work? ☐

3 Do you enjoy travelling? ☐

4 When are you planning to go back to Australia? ☐

5 What sort of social life do you have? ☐

6 Do you live in a city or in the country? ☐

7 What are your plans for the future? ☐

2 | *Going places USA*

VOCABULARY

Divide the words in the list below into three groups according to whether you would use them to talk about travelling by:

plane	train	both
		announcement

announcement   arrivals   boarding pass
baggage retrieval   cabin   catch   charter
check in   compartment   connection   crew
customs   crowd   delay   departure lounge
duty-free   fare   flight   ground staff
information desk   passenger   passport control
platform   reservation   take off   terminal
transfer area   waiting room

GRAMMAR

1 Look at these airport jobs. Write down things that people with these jobs do. Use verbs from the list below.

fly   search   check   weigh   serve   look after
authorise   stop   carry

1   Passport control officer

_____

2   Customs officer

_____

3   Flight attendant

_____

4   Pilot

_____

5   Airline check-in clerk

_____

6   Porter

_____

2 Look at the pictures. Write sentences saying what the people are doing.

Picture 1   *The flight attendant is serving drinks.*

Picture 2   _____

Picture 3   _____

Picture 4   _____

3 Write the verb in brackets in the present continuous or the present simple.

1   I think she _____ coffee with Jane in the cafeteria at the moment. (have)

2   I _____ this exercise. (not understand)

3   He's a baseball coach. He _____ at the city stadium. (work)

4   About 170 planes _____ at or _____ from Atlanta airport every hour. (land, take off)

5   Peter _____ history at college, but he _____ at the museum for the summer vacation. (study, work)

6   She usually _____ her holiday with her parents, but this summer she _____ to Greece. (spend, fly)

7   Most children _____ sweets. (like)

8   I _____ for Chicago in an hour. I _____ two meetings tomorrow. (leave, attend)

9 I never _____ coffee. (drink)

10 He _____ to stay at the Ritz, because it
   is very expensive. (not want)

LISTENING

1 The sentences below are travel plans. Put a tick
(✓) by the sentences which you could use to
talk about a business trip.

a We're hiring a car so we can see the area. ☐

b Then, at three, you're seeing the people
   from the bank. ☐

c I'm staying with friends until Monday. ☐

d I'm going to Rome for three days to
   do some sightseeing. ☐

e At 9.30 you're attending a meeting. ☐

2 📟 Listen to three people talking about their
travel plans. Decide where they are going and
how they are travelling. Which speaker is
travelling for business?

	Destination	**Means of transport**
Speaker 1	_____	_____
Speaker 2	_____	_____
Speaker 3	_____	_____

3 📟 Listen to Speakers 2 and 3 again and
complete their diaries with their arrangements.

Speaker 2

7.00 *take train to Boston* _____

8.30 _____

9.30 _____

1.00 _____

3.00 _____

5.30 _____

Speaker 3

Thursday 16 at 10.30 _____

Thursday 16 at 9.45 _____

Thursday 16 – Monday 20 _____

Monday 20 – Thursday 23 _____

Thursday 23 _____

Thursday 23 – Monday 27 _____

Monday 27 at 12.00 _____

SOUNDS

📟 Listen and correct the statements below.
Change the stressed word each time.

1 They're going to *Toronto* for their summer
   holiday. (Vancouver)
   No, they're going to Vancouver.

2 They're leaving on *Monday*. (Saturday)

3 They're travelling by *train*. (by plane)

4 They're staying at a *camp site*. (hotel)

5 They're coming back on *6th August*. (29th July)

WRITING

1 Write sentences for Speakers 2 and 3 describing
their arrangements.

Speaker 2

She's taking the train to Boston at 7 o'clock.
_____

_____

_____

Speaker 3

_____

_____

_____

2 Think of three people you know. Write
sentences saying what they do and what they
are probably doing at the moment.

My mother works for an advertising agency in
Lisbon. On Mondays she usually spends the
day at the office, so she is probably working
at the office now.

_____

_____

_____

_____

_____

_____

_____

_____

_____

3 *All dressed in red*

VOCABULARY

Complete these sentences with words from the list below. Use the correct form of the verbs and nouns.

ceremony   celebrate   groom   registry office
horoscope   veil

1   The _____ arrives at the church with the best man.

2   The bride wears a _____ over her face.

3   A holy man studies the _____ of the bride and groom to choose the right day.

4   Chinese weddings have three different

_____ .

5   Many weddings only take place at a

_____ .

6   After _____ their marriage separately for several days, the bride and groom finally get together.

READING

1   You are going to read a passage about traditional wedding entertainment in Egyptian villages. What sort of entertainment is traditional in your country?

2   Read *The night of the henna* and find out what sort of wedding entertainment is traditional in Egyptian villages.

3   Read the passage again and put these events in the right order. Number them 1 to 7.

a   The guests take their seats. ☐

b   The poet appears on the platform. ☐

c   The guests go to the mosque to pray. ☐

d   The trousseau is presented. ☐

e   The local dignitaries welcome the poet. ☐

f   The children come into the square. ☐

g   The poet has a sleep. ☐

The night of the henna

Weddings in many Egyptian villages take place traditionally after the farmers have sold the summer harvest. This is the only time of year when they have enough money to go into town and buy a trousseau for the future bride. The wedding festivities begin on the eve of the wedding which is called the 'night of the henna'. During the 'night of the henna' the bride's hands and feet are painted with henna. This ceremony, which takes place in the privacy of the bride's home, marks the beginning of the wedding festivities.

But the highlight of the day is the arrival of the poet. Although today many families have abandoned this traditional form of entertainment, the few remaining poets always receive an enthusiastic welcome.

The poet and his musicians usually arrive during the early afternoon, before the henna ceremony. After greeting him at the entrance to the village, a few local dignitaries take him to the house of the host family. There, he takes refreshments before having a sleep to prepare him for the long evening ahead. After having an early supper, he and his partners tune their instruments.

During the day, the village square is prepared for the evening performance. A platform is set up for the poet and his musicians. Mats are placed around the platform for the guests, and seats of honour are reserved for the local dignitaries. The children are the first to crowd into the square and sit as close to the platform as possible. After going to the mosque to pray, the wedding guests make their way to their seats. Finally, when everyone is settled, the poet appears on the platform. He is greeted with cries of joy, the entire audience is attentive to his slightest change of expression.

Every poet always tells the same story, the epic of Abou Zeid El Hilali. The poet never begins the story at the beginning, just as he never reaches the end. His art lies in his ability to catch the listeners' attention and control their sympathies and emotions. There are a number of interruptions during the narrative for the musicians to play and the whole evening's entertainment lasts for several hours.

The wedding ceremony takes place on the following day. The musicians play all afternoon during the presentation of the bride's trousseau to her groom's family.

4 Answer the questions and try to guess the meanings of the words.

1 *harvest*: What do the farmers grow and sell at the end of the summer?

2 *dignitaries*: Are these likely to be important or unimportant people?

3 *trousseau*: What do the bride's parents give to the groom's parents?

4 *highlight*: Is this likely to be an important or an unimportant moment of the day?

5 *refreshments*: What are his hosts likely to give him after his journey?

GRAMMAR

1 Look back at the passage and underline the time expressions with *during* and *for*.

2 Look at these sentences about the passage and underline the action which happens first.

1 Weddings in many Egyptian villages take place after the farmers have sold the summer harvest.

2 After greeting the poet at the village entrance, the dignitaries take him to the host family.

3 He takes refreshments before having a sleep.

4 After having an early supper, the poet and his partners tune their instruments.

5 The wedding guests make their way to their seats after praying at the mosque.

3 Look back at the passage and join these sentences. Start with *after*.

1 The farmers sell the summer harvest. They buy their daughters' trousseaus.

After *the farmers have sold the summer harvest, they buy their daughters' trousseaus.*

2 The bride's hands and feet are painted with henna. The wedding festivities can begin.

After _____

_____

3 The poet has a sleep. He tunes his instruments.

After _____

_____

4 The guests take their seats. The poet appears on the platform.

_____

5 The wedding ceremony takes place. The bride's family present her trousseau.

_____

_____

LISTENING

1 These sentences describe three different British family customs: Christmas, Easter and the tooth fairy. Put the sentences into three groups.

1 After they have gone to bed, Father Christmas brings their presents.

2 Before getting dressed, the children run into the garden.

3 Before going to bed, they put their stockings near the fireplace.

4 After losing a tooth, the children put it under their pillow at bedtime.

5 After eating all the chocolate eggs, they never want to eat lunch.

6 After they have gone to sleep, I carefully exchange the tooth for a coin.

7 Before hiding the chocolate eggs in the garden, he makes sure they're both asleep.

8 Before they have breakfast, the children open their presents.

2 📼 Listen to three people talking about the three customs. Write the number of each sentence above next to the speaker who says it.

	Sentences	Custom
Speaker 1	_____	_____
Speaker 2	_____	_____
Speaker 3	_____	_____

WRITING

Do you have similar customs in your country? Write a few sentences describing a custom.

_____

_____

_____

_____

_____

Are you a couch potato?

VOCABULARY

1 Tick (✓) the adjectives which are positive and put a circle round those which are negative.

awful brilliant boring dreadful dull
entertaining exciting fun great relaxing
superb terrific wonderful terrible frightening

2 Write down an activity which you find:

exciting *sailing*
boring
fun
relaxing
terrific
terrible

GRAMMAR

1 Match the questions 1 to 5 with answers a to e. Put the correct letters in the boxes.

1 Do you often go to the cinema? ☐
2 How often do you entertain friends? ☐
3 When do you usually go out? ☐
4 Do you enjoy watching TV? ☐
5 What do you usually do at the weekend? ☐

a On Saturday evenings.
b We go out walking with friends.
c No, not very often, I'm afraid.
d Once or twice a week.
e Yes, very much indeed.

2 Put these words in order and write sentences.

1 to rarely I out restaurants go very
I rarely go out to restaurants.

2 watching the every enjoys football on night television Saturday he
_____
_____

3 I twice holiday away on go year a
_____
_____

4 friends ever entertain home at they their hardly
_____
_____

5 she the cycling most goes park mornings in
_____
_____

6 take never children the to we cinema the
_____
_____

3 Write sentences saying how often you do these things.

1 go on holiday
I go on holiday twice a year.

2 go shopping
_____

3 buy a newspaper
_____

4 play cards
_____

5 listen to music
_____

4 Write sentences saying what you do:

every day
I watch television every day.

most mornings
_____

twice a week
_____

once a year
_____

hardly ever
_____

never
_____

SOUNDS

🔊 Listen to these sentences and underline the stressed words.

1 I adore going to discos with friends.

2 I really hate staying in; I get so bored.

3 I quite enjoy gardening but don't like collecting the leaves.

4 I can't stand cleaning the house, it's such dull work.

5 I don't really mind staying at home with the children.

🔊 Now listen again and check. Say the sentences aloud.

READING

1 The passages describe national passions in two countries. Look quickly at the passages and choose a suitable heading for each one.

1 National service in Thailand.
2 Queuing is the national passion.
3 Weekend entertainment.
4 Gambling is a very important aspect of life.

2 In which of the passages are you likely to find these words?

winners   orderly   push   bet   bus-stop   draw wait   temptation   chance   stand   lottery number patiently   luck

Read the passages and check.

3 Read passage A and find three gambling activities that Thais enjoy.

4 Read passage B and decide if it is serious or humorous.

WRITING

1 Write a few sentences describing a national passion in your country.

2 Write a few sentences describing one of your favourite leisure activities.

A

Most Thais find it difficult to resist the temptation to gamble. There are national lottery tickets on sale at every street corner, and each bus ticket you buy has a lottery number on it. Even conscription into the national service is determined by luck. If you draw a black ticket you do your national service, if you draw a red one you don't!

Even the poorest paid workers occasionally get together a few *baht* and play a game of chance. Not to take part may be considered anti-social.

Gambling, for most people, provides a relatively cheap form of entertainment, is a favourite topic of conversation and, since winners inevitably treat their friends, it provides endless opportunities for getting together and having a good time. Some forms of gambling, cock-fighting, fish-fighting and betting on the outcome of a Thai boxing bout, not only provide entertainment but can also become full-time occupations.

B Most people are rather shy about it, and always deny that they adore it.

In most countries, if people are waiting at a bus-stop they stand around in a disorderly fashion. When the bus arrives they make a dash for it and push their way on. An English person, even if he or she is alone, forms an orderly queue of one and waits patiently.

At weekends, the Londoner queues up at the bus-stop, travels out to the country, queues up for a boat, then queues up for tea, then queues up for ice cream, then joins a few more odd queues just for the fun of it, then queues up at a bus-stop and has the time of his/her life. For most people this would be a boring way of spending a free day, for the English it is an exciting day out.

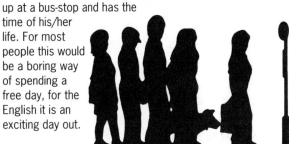

LISTENING

1 🔊 Listen to four people talking about how they like to spend their spare time. Note down their favourite activities.

	Activity	How often
Speaker 1	_____	_____
Speaker 2	_____	_____
Speaker 3	_____	_____
Speaker 4	_____	_____

2 🔊 Listen again and find out how often they enjoy doing these activities. Complete the chart in activity 1 above.

5 | *Face the music*

VOCABULARY

1 Underline the words that describe how someone feels.

amazing   boring   delighted   embarrassing
excited   frightened   puzzled   surprised

What do the words you underlined have in common?

2 Complete the sentences below with words from the list.

1   Discussions about the weather are extremely *boring* .

2   I find talking about money problems very _____ .

3   She was quite _____ when her car broke down on a country road at midnight.

4   He was _____ to see us because he hadn't received our message.

5   Some of the new medical techniques are really _____ !

6   I was _____ to hear about your wedding plans.

3 Rewrite the sentences with adjectives ending in *-ing*.

1   Stories of the supernatural fascinate me.
   Stories of the supernatural are fascinating.

2   Opera doesn't interest me at all.

   _____

3   Rock music excites people of all ages.

   _____

4   Watching television relaxes me.

   _____

5   Politics bores many people.

   _____

   _____

READING

1 Read the passages A to G and decide which question they all answer.

1   How do you like to spend your evenings?

2   What are your favourite conversation topics?

3   What topics do you avoid discussing?

2 Underline the adjectives in the passages which describe how people feel about these topics of conversation.

local politics   personal relationships
travel   football

3 What adjectives describe these topics?

food   *interesting* _____

world news   _____

money   _____

music   _____

4 Which passage(s) is/are closest to your ideas?

Write down adjectives you would choose to describe the topics in activities 2 and 3.

A Well, we talk about all sorts of things, but we usually end the evening discussing local politics. Most of us are interested in the community, so there's always plenty to talk about. Some people even get a bit annoyed, but we never have serious arguments. **Harry**

B Lots of different things. We try to avoid talking about personal relationships. Most people get embarrassed if the conversation becomes too personal, so we tend to keep it on a general level. **Alan**

C We keep away from religion and politics. If you want to create a friendly atmosphere and help people feel relaxed there are many other things which are more likely to interest everybody. Travel, for instance, is a good ice-breaker. **Fred**

D Well, we seem to spend a lot of time talking about food. It's something that we all enjoy. It's one of those universal topics that most people find interesting. **Mary**

E Our conversations are usually about daily life and people we meet. We don't talk about the world news because it is so depressing. Money is another subject we avoid because it can be embarrassing. **Linda**

F Football is a favourite subject as most of us are supporters. We get very excited when there is an important match on. People who don't know us well are often very surprised to hear us arguing, they don't realise that it's just good fun. **Christopher**

G We are all mad about jazz. The music scene is really exciting because there are so many exciting new bands around today so we never get bored with it. We don't talk about much else really, except sometimes our personal relationships – boyfriends, that sort of thing. **Eva**

SOUNDS

1 Complete these sentences with a question tag.

1 Well, we aren't doing very well, _are we?_

2 You are sure she's coming, _____

3 You do like staying up late, _____

4 It's not them again, _____

5 You don't really expect me to agree to that,

_____

6 Excuse me. This is the right way to the station,

_____

2 📼 Listen to each sentence and write Q in the box if you think the speaker is asking a real question and A if you think the speaker expects agreement.

1 ☐ 2 ☐ 3 ☐ 4 ☐ 5 ☐ 6 ☐

3 📼 Listen to the sentences again and decide which adjective you can use to describe how the speakers sound.

friendly angry bored unhappy impatient polite

1 _unhappy_

2 _____

3 _____

4 _____

5 _____

6 _____

WRITING

Write a short paragraph in answer to one of the questions in *Reading* activity 1.

_____

_____

_____

_____

_____

_____

_____

_____

_____

_____

_____

VOCABULARY AND SOUNDS

1 Write these words in the correct column of the chart. Complete the noun and adjective columns and underline the stressed syllables.

ambitious   confidence   honest   idealism
independent   intelligent   patience   reliable
sincerity   talented

noun	adjective	opposite
ambition	ambitious	unambitious
_____	_____	_____
_____	_____	_____
_____	_____	_____
_____	_____	_____
_____	_____	_____
_____	_____	_____
_____	_____	_____
_____	_____	_____
_____	_____	_____

Put a tick (✓) if the stressed syllable is the same in both the noun and the adjective form. Put a cross (✗) if it is different.

🔲 Now listen and check.

2 Complete the third column of the chart with words which mean the opposite of the adjectives. Use your dictionary if necessary.

• • • • • • • • • • • • • **A** • • • • • • • • • • • •

I was playing in a club when I heard of this new, talented musician. In my break I walked over to the place where he was performing. I think he was wearing a dark, three-button Italian suit with a black tie. I knocked on the dressing room door to say hello. I was immediately impressed by his open, down-to-earth manner. After that, we saw a lot of each other. We both loved sport as well as music. We both came from the north so we had a lot in common. But I think it was his sense of humour that I appreciated most of all.

• • • • • • • • • • • • • **B** • • • • • • • • • • • •

He's more than just a good friend! We first met at a party when I was studying. Ours was an unlikely friendship at first. He was a dreamer and he enjoyed solitary things like reading and cooking. I was much more active and sociable and I liked team sports. He was understanding and whenever I got into trouble he was always there to help me. He is married with a family now but it hasn't changed our relationship. I still feel just as relaxed when we are together.

• • • • • • • • • • • • • **C** • • • • • • • • • • • •

I met her for the first time when I was hiking in Scotland. She was the guide and I was very impressed by her patience and self-control when things got difficult. Our friendship grew as we got to know each other better and I came to admire her determination. At the end of the week I invited her to stay at my parents' home. We have very different personalities: she is a born optimist and an extrovert. But that is probably why we get on so well. I haven't seen her for nearly a year because I live in Spain, but she writes at least once a week.

• • • • • • • • • • • • • **D** • • • • • • • • • • • •

That night I had played badly and wasn't feeling very happy. Somebody said he was at the club and wanted to meet me. I was excited because he was quite famous. I remember he was wearing a fashionable black overcoat with a velvet collar when he came into the dressing room. We had a drink together the next day. Later, we even did concerts around the country together. We played golf most mornings, table tennis in the afternoons and music in the evenings. With us it's like speaking the same language.

• • • • • • • • • • • • • **E** • • • • • • • • • • • •

She was a member of a group I was taking into the mountains for a week. I immediately felt she would be a good friend. At the time, I was working away from home and was lonely. She was very kind and we had very similar tastes. I came to rely on her and turn to her for advice. I was often away working and it was marvellous to have a real friend to write to. She was naturally quite shy, so I think I helped her meet other people. We don't see so much of each other nowadays because she lives abroad but that has not affected our friendship at all.

READING

1 In the passage five people are talking about their best friends and how they first met them. Read the passage and find out how they met.

2 Underline the personal qualities that the people attribute to their friends.

3 The five parts of the passage can be paired together. Read the passage again and decide which parts go together. Which part is the odd-one-out?

GRAMMAR

1 Rewrite the sentences in the past simple or the past continuous.

1 He played golf.
He was playing golf.

2 She was staying with a friend.

3 They worked hard.

4 We weren't living here.

5 I didn't listen.

2 Complete the sentences with verbs in the past simple or the past continuous.

1 I *was playing* in a club when I first *saw* her. (play, see)

2 They _____ when the police _____ . (fight, arrive)

3 They _____ around South America at the time. (travel)

4 The last time they _____ , he _____ in Spain. (meet, work)

5 She _____ to see us when we _____ with friends in London. (come, stay)

6 He _____ his first novel when he _____ . (write, die)

3 Look back at the passages in *Reading* and write down three things that were in progress at a specific time in the past.

1 *He was wearing an Italian suit.*

2 _____

3 _____

4 _____

4 Complete the sentences with information from the passages.

1 I was playing in a club *when I heard of this talented, new musician.*

2 I met her when I _____ .

3 When he came into the dressing room, he _____ .

4 We first met at a party when I _____ .

5 Write sentences about what you were doing at these times.

two hours ago

_____

at 8 o'clock this morning

_____

on Saturday night

_____

last Sunday morning

_____

in May last year

_____

in September 1994

_____

WRITING

Read again the part of the passage that was the odd-one-out in *Reading*. Write a passage to go with it.

_____

_____

_____

_____

_____

_____

7 | # *The way things used to be*

VOCABULARY

Complete these sentences with words from the list below.

behave   competitions   neighbours   outings

prize   trip

1   There used to be a special _____ for the winner.

2   My father used to _____ like a boy.

3   They used to go on a wonderful _____ to the seaside every year.

4   He used to organise games and _____.

5   The family used to look forward to the _____.

6   He used to invite the _____.

SOUNDS

🔲 Listen to the sentences in *Vocabulary*. Notice how you do not hear the 'd' sound in *used to*.

Say the sentences aloud.

READING

1   Read *The selective memory*. Are the writer's memories mainly happy or unhappy?

2   Write down three things we learn about the place where the writer lived as a child.
1   *The writer lived in a small village.*
2   _____
3   _____
4   _____

3   Read the passage again and write down four things the writer used to do.
1   *She used to do her school work very quickly.*
2   _____
3   _____
4   _____
5   _____

4   Rewrite the underlined sentences in the passage using *used to*.
1   *I used to spend the evenings messing around in the village harbour.*
2   _____
3   _____
4   _____
5   _____
6   _____
7   _____

5   Tick the sentence that best explains why the writer describes her memory as selective.
1   Because she only remembers the happy moments of childhood.
2   Because she has a bad memory for particular events.
3   Because she can only remember sensations.

Do you have a selective memory?

LISTENING

1   🔲 Listen to three people talking about their memories of childhood. Put a tick (✔) if their memories are mainly happy and a cross (✗) if they are mainly unhappy.

Speaker 1: ☐

Speaker 2: ☐

Speaker 3: ☐

2   Which speaker do you think wrote the passage *The selective memory*?

_____

The selective memory

Long, warm evenings <u>spent messing around the village harbour</u>. Watching the fishermen going about their business. I remember a general sensation of well-being. It never used to be cold as it always seems to be when I stroll around the seafront today. The endless days spent indoors because of the steady rain are forgotten. Only the sunshine and warmth remain as a memory.

<u>I lived in a little seaside village</u> which was full of holidaymakers in the summer and deserted the rest of the year. <u>We ran free</u>, a gang of local children of all ages. School work was never a big issue; we used to do it quickly so we could go off down to the village. We used to devour enormous slices of bread and jam before pulling on our bathing costumes and heading for the harbour to join the other kids.

Our main occupation during the summer months was <u>jumping off the harbour wall</u> into the sea. We used to encourage one another to jump higher and higher. The most admired feat used to be the big jump from the top of the small, domed lighthouse which was the highest point along the sea wall. Only the most intrepid members of the gang used to do this one.

But our greatest admiration was for the beautiful, <u>young people who drove speed boats around the bay</u>. We used to sit on the wall watching these sophisticated creatures who lived in far-away towns and who spent their holidays sun bathing and water skiing. We used to dream of becoming members of their exclusive club and going for trips around the bay. But <u>they never mixed with us locals</u>.

Sometimes we went fishing off the rocks and caught dozens of silver mackerel. We used to spend hours in the rock pools which were only visible at low tide. We didn't use to do things according to the time of day, but instead, <u>we followed the rhythm of the sea</u>. Our clock was the timetable high up on the wall at the entrance to the harbour which informed the fishermen of the daily times of high and low tides.

The memory selects only parts of childhood, the rest is pushed into dark corners. We never remember the whole truth, only bits and pieces picked up here and there. Memories dissolve into one another and form a blurred whole made up of sensations, not of particular events.

My own memory has only kept the happy moments of a free and easy childhood, but I wonder if this is always the case?

3 🔲 Listen again and write down two memories for each speaker.

Speaker 1 *I used to spend hours sitting in a tree reading.*

_____

Speaker 2 _____

_____

Speaker 3 _____

_____

_____

WRITING

1 Think about your childhood and write down one word which you associate with each of the words in the list below.

boring   miserable   wonderful   special   fortunate
endless   dream   fun   enormous

_____

_____

2 Write five sentences about your childhood using words from the list above.

1 _____

_____

2 _____

_____

3 _____

_____

4 _____

_____

5 _____

_____

3 Was your childhood mainly happy or unhappy? Write a short paragraph describing how you remember spending your time as a child.

_____

_____

_____

_____

_____

_____

Cold, lost, hungry and alone

GRAMMAR

1 Underline the action which happens first.

1 When <u>I got up</u> I had a cup of black coffee.

2 I phoned my mother as soon as I reached the station.

3 She was going to meet her brother when she arrived in Rome.

4 They drove away as soon as the traffic lights turned green.

5 He started to panic when he realised he was lost.

6 I waited at the information desk until she arrived.

2 Complete the sentences with *while, as* or *when*. There may be more than one possibility.

1 *When* _____ I arrived at the airport, I phoned my friend.

2 _____ I was eating at the restaurant, they were looking for me in the bar.

3 I was walking to the departure lounge _____ I heard the announcement.

4 He was having a coffee _____ they attacked him.

5 A man stopped them _____ they were walking along the street.

6 Just _____ they were coming out of the shop, the woman walked past.

3 Join the sentences with *when, as, while, as soon as,* or *until*. Write two sentences for each.

1 She was working. The boss walked in.
She was working when the boss walked in.
While she was working the boss walked in.

2 They were waiting at reception.
The police were searching the room.

_____

_____

3 I was feeling very lonely. My friend called me.

_____

_____

4 A group of people crowded round us.
We were standing in a queue.

_____

_____

5 He stood up.
The teacher walked into the room.

_____

_____

6 I had to wait for an hour.
They checked my passport.

_____

_____

4 Complete the sentences with the past simple or the past continuous form of the verbs in brackets. There may be more than one possibility.

1 I _____ my lunch when the flight attendant _____ my meal tray away. (eat, take)

2 The captain _____ over the loud-speaker that we _____ back to Gatwick Airport. (announce, fly)

3 When I _____ of the window I _____ that we were flying north. (look out, see)

4 Everyone _____ speaking when the captain _____ us that there was a bomb alert. (stop, tell)

5 As the flight attendant _____ the hand-baggage compartments, the captain told us that we were going to make an emergency landing in Rouen. (check)

6 Everyone was quiet until the plane _____ the ground. (touch)

7 As soon as the plane _____ people _____ towards the emergency exits. (land, push)

8 When we _____ in the terminal, ground staff _____ hot tea. (arrive, serve)

READING

1 Read the passage and choose the best title.

1 An exciting day out

2 An accident

3 A disastrous fishing trip

4 Summer days

Our first fishing trip of the summer was a memorable affair. My brother Peter and I got up at dawn and packed our fishing equipment. The sun was shining and the sea was calm when we climbed into the little motor boat tied to the quayside. We knew that we wouldn't be able to go back in again until the evening high-tide, so we had prepared a picnic and taken some bottles of drink.

As soon as we reached the point, we stopped the engine and got out our fishing lines. We were beginning to get bored, so we decided to move a bit further out to sea. That was when things started to go wrong. As we were getting the lines ready again, Peter stood on a fishing hook and got it stuck in his foot. When he sat down with a bump, the boat started to rock violently and the picnic basket fell overboard. Peter asked me to get the hook out of his foot, so I fiddled with it in vain until he cried out to me to stop because of the pain. Poor Pete was very shaken and he lay on his back in the bottom of the boat until he felt better.

We didn't feel very much like fishing any more, so we decided to head back to the beach. I started the engine, and we chugged sadly homewards. We had run out of petrol. Peter opened the storage chest to get out the spare petrol-can we always take with us. He looked puzzled for a moment, then he looked alarmed. The can wasn't there and he didn't remember putting it on the boat. We had no choice but to row back, and that would take us hours.

While we were discussing where to head for, we realised, to our horror, that the wind was blowing and the sea was getting quite rough. We felt really worried when we discovered that the life-jackets weren't on the boat either. We rowed towards the nearest beach, but after about twenty minutes we still didn't seem to be getting any closer.

Just as we were getting frightened, a fishing boat appeared round the point. For a few moments I thought the boat was going to go past us, so we stood up and shouted. The people on the boat saw us, and as soon as it was close enough, the fishermen threw us a rope and towed us back to the harbour. We were so relieved that we just sat back and enjoyed the ride.

2 Read the story again and decide where these sentences go. The sentences are in the order in which they appear in the story.

1 The tide was going out as we chugged out of the harbour.

2 We sat there for nearly an hour, but we didn't get so much as a single pull on the lines.

3 In the end I gave it a violent pull and it came out.

4 Suddenly, after about fifteen minutes, the engine stopped.

3 Write sentences to describe how the writer and her brother felt at these times.

1 When they had been fishing for nearly an hour.
  She was bored.

2 When the writer had pulled the hook out of Peter's foot.
  _____

3 When they started to chug towards home.
  _____

4 When Peter couldn't find the spare petrol can.
  _____

5 When they discovered that the life-jackets weren't on the boat.
  _____

6 When a fishing boat appeared round the point.
  _____

WRITING

Can you think of a similar incident that happened to you or to somebody you know? Write a short paragraph describing:

– what happened

– how it happened

– what the circumstances were

– how you felt

– what you did

_____

_____

_____

_____

_____

_____

17

GRAMMAR

1 Complete these sentences with *who* or *which*.

1 Coffee plants, _____ only grow in the tropics, need a hot, moist climate.

2 Sofia, _____ is the capital of Bulgaria, has a population of over one million.

3 Herman Melville, _____ wrote *Moby Dick*, was one of the greatest American writers.

4 Many of the great jazz musicians, _____ came from New Orleans, could not read music.

5 *Coffea arabica*, _____ came originally from Arabia, is a popular variety of coffee.

2 Match the sentences 1 to 5 with a suitable sentence a to e. Rewrite the sentences with *who* or *which* using the extra information.

1 Coffee was common in most of Europe by the 17th century.

2 Brazil is the largest South American country.

3 Budapest is the capital of Hungary.

4 Picasso influenced many modern painters.

5 Conan Doyle created the detective Sherlock Holmes.

a He died in Paris in 1973.

b It came from the Middle East.

c It is on the Danube.

d He was a 19th-century English author.

e It occupies nearly half the continent.

1 _____
  _____

2 _____
  _____

3 _____
  _____

4 _____
  _____

5 _____
  _____

3 Put the words in order and make sentences. There are two possible sentences.

1 Bell the who American was telephone invented
  Bell, who was American, invented the telephone.
  Bell, who invented the telephone, was American.

2 Columbus in Italian reached who America was 1492.
  Columbus, _____
  _____

3 Cervantes 16th in wrote the century lived *Don Quixote* who
  Cervantes, _____
  _____

4 Walt Disney Mickey Mouse began career in who his 1920 created
  Walt Disney, _____
  _____

5 Rotterdam is Sea world's North the port is on largest which the
  Rotterdam, _____
  _____

6 Tea a in India warm grown and requires China which is climate
  Tea, _____
  _____

READING

1 Read the passage and choose the best title.

1 Chocolate – the passion of a lifetime

2 The Chocolate Munchers

3 Chocolate – a new art form

4 The last word in good taste

The aroma of chocolate perfumes the air of the rue d'Assas in Paris. Entering Christian Constant's state-of-the-art boutique, you find yourself in the kingdom of Paris's king of chocolate, where the humble cocoa bean is being turned into mouth-watering chocolate Easter eggs.

Constant, who is a chef, admits that chocolate is his passion and main interest in life. He first developed a fascination for chocolate when he was working for Gaston Lenôtre, a famous French patissier.

Every year he has a theme for decorating Easter eggs: this year his decorations are inspired by art nouveau. Tonight he has a dinner for 130 to organise and he has to prepare a metre-high art nouveau decorated Easter egg by midday tomorrow. This, for Constant, is a normal schedule.

Constant believes that his chocolate creations are as much a work of art as other sculptures. It is, therefore, understandable that the restaurant he opened last month, which is in the style of the 1930s, is situated in the National Monuments Museum in Paris. During the day the restaurant is a chocolate tearoom and offers chocolate in every imaginable form. Customers can choose from a selection of sweet chocolate desserts or try the more exotic spicy chocolates. Constant is also a 'nose', working closely with the French Institute of Taste. He is capable of identifying 450 different tastes and flavours. Constant explains that the mouth, which can only taste four things – salt, sweet, acid and bitter – is 'stupid' in comparison to the nose. He believes that the nose is everything.

In his book *The Taste of Chocolate*, he explains how in 1502 Christopher Columbus came across an island and went ashore. He was greeted by an Indian chief bearing gifts, among which were huge sacks of beans which Columbus thought was the local currency. To his surprise, they prepared a drink for him. But Columbus, who disliked the odd bitter taste, continued on his travels, ignorant of the fact that he had just tasted cocoa. Like Columbus, Constant travels the cocoa countries where he checks quality and works with local experts. Quality can vary depending on the region, year and methods of preparation. According to Constant, Venezuela and Trinidad have the best.

Constant, who is a hard worker, only sleeps three hours a night. He talks long into the night with members of a club he has formed. The club is called The Chocolate Munchers. Their main official activity is to get together for monthly dinners where they eat a very tiny dinner and masses of chocolate desserts.

'I am an addict,' Constant admits, 'and I don't want to be cured!'

2 Write down five facts about Christian Constant.

1 *He has a boutique.* _____

2 _____

3 _____

4 _____

5 _____

3 Read the passage again and underline five non-defining relative clauses.

4 Decide where these phrases can go in the passage.

1 ..., which already has over 150 members,

2 ..., which only serves full meals in the evening,

3 ..., who was lost in a storm,

5 Which of these words can you use to describe how things taste?

aroma   spicy   bitter   flavour   sweet   perfume
mouth-watering   acid

What 'sense' do the extra words refer to?

SOUNDS

Write these words from the passage in the correct column and complete the chart. Underline the stressed syllable.

fascination   prepare   explain   decoration
selection   creation   organise

Noun	**Verb**
fascination	*fascinate*
_____	_____
_____	_____
_____	_____
_____	_____

Put a tick (✓) if the stressed syllable is the same in both the noun and the verb. Put a cross (✗) if it is different.

▶ Now listen and check. Say the words aloud.

SOUNDS

1 🔲 Listen and say these sentences aloud. Try to sound polite.

1 Could you lend me your Student's Book, please?

2 Excuse me. Could you turn the radio down, please?

3 Would you mind taking it back to the shop for me?

4 Could you give me his new address, please?

5 Would you mind giving us a lift into town?

6 I wonder if you could tell me when the next train to Cardiff is?

2 Match these responses with the requests in the sentences in 1.

1 ☐ 2 ☐ 3 ☐ 4 ☐ 5 ☐ 6 ☐

a Oh dear! I'm awfully sorry. I didn't realise it was so loud.

b I'm afraid not. You see, I'm not going into town this evening.

c No, I won't have time. You'll just have to take it in yourself.

d Ten forty-five from platform three.

e I'm afraid I haven't got my address book with me. I'm sorry.

f Why? Have you forgotten yours again?

Put a tick (✓) if the response is positive, a cross (✗) if it is negative and a question mark (?) if it isn't certain.

3 🔲 Listen. Which responses sound polite and friendly? Which sound impolite?

GRAMMAR AND FUNCTIONS

1 Find four verbs in the sentences in *Sounds* activity 1 which have two objects. Write down four more verbs which can take two objects.

2 Rewrite these sentences without using the preposition.

1 She bought a box of chocolates for me.
   She bought me a box of chocolates.

2 They showed photos of their home to her.
   _____

3 He sold ten computers to the company.
   _____

4 We gave a bunch of flowers to our hostess.
   _____

5 He offered a seat to the elderly gentleman.
   _____

6 I read a story to my children.
   _____

3 Write suitable requests using verbs with two objects for these situations. Use these verbs:

lend   pass   give   take   send   order

1 You have forgotten your wallet. You can't pay the waiter. You are with a friend.
   Would you mind lending me some money?

2 You are sitting at the table with a friend. You can't reach the salt and pepper.
   _____

3 You want a travel brochure. You phone a travel agency.
   _____

4 You need a taxi. You phone your secretary.
   _____

5 Your friend has a business report. You want to see it.
   _____

6 Your mother is in hospital. She wants some magazines. Your friend is going to see her.
   _____

VOCABULARY

1 Which of the adjectives below could you use to describe a person's feelings and which a person's behaviour? Put them into two groups: *feelings* and *behaviour*.

angry anxious bored casual cross dishonest
embarrassed friendly hurt immoral mean
pleased polite reluctant surprised worried

2 Can you think of situations where you have felt hurt, embarrassed or angry?

READING

1 Look quickly at the passage about national customs in different countries. Put a tick (✓) by the national customs which are described.

punctuality ☐   greetings ☐

use of titles ☐   gift-giving ☐

2 These statements about the passage are false. Read the passage and correct the statements.

1 Kissing is not a common form of French greeting.

_____

2 German hospitality is very informal.

_____

3 Greek men shake hands and women kiss each other.

_____

4 Roses or chrysanthemums are an acceptable gift for a French hostess.

_____

3 Write a sentence for each country saying what gift you should give your host/hostess if you are invited for dinner. Use a verb with two objects where possible.

1 _____

_____

2 _____

_____

3 _____

_____

WRITING

Write a similar paragraph describing customary greetings and gift-giving in your country.

_____

_____

_____

_____

Greece
There are no rules for greeting. Greeks may shake hands, embrace and/or kiss at the first and every meeting. Greek hospitality is sincere, incredibly generous, and sometimes overwhelming. Be careful not to praise a specific object or the host may insist on giving it to you. If you are invited to a Greek home, take flowers or a cake for the hostess.

France
The handshake is an important part of normal social relations in France and not just something you do the first time you meet someone. It is done on greeting and parting, between strangers, close relatives, and even children. Kissing is also a common form of greeting between close friends and relatives. It is done two or three times, alternating cheeks. Do not be surprised to see men embracing.

An invitation to visit someone's home, even after long acquaintance, is rare. But for that occasion, a bottle of Scotch, a cake or, even better, a small gift of flowers (not red roses or chrysanthemums which are a reminder of death) or chocolates for the hostess will be appreciated. Gifts that appeal to the intellect or aesthetics are especially appreciated.

Germany
Handshakes all around are customary on meeting and leaving. Germans do not kiss.

A German's home is his private castle and invitations to German homes are a special privilege. A man should bring flowers, which he will unwrap in the entrance hall and present to the hostess upon greeting her. Avoid red roses because of the romantic connotation and do not offer an even number of flowers as this is considered to bring bad luck.

A thank-you note should be sent within a few days for any hospitality.

11 | *Do it now!*

VOCABULARY

Match the verbs on the left with the nouns on the right.

throw away	the table
do	the heating
make	the cat
lay	the rubbish
tidy up	the lunch
clean	the washing up
turn on	the cooker
put out	the house

GRAMMAR

1 Put the words in order and form sentences.

1 gas yet hasn't the paid he bill.
He hasn't paid the gas bill yet.

2 booked yet you tickets have theatre the?
_____

3 interested are in archaeology you still?
_____

4 already the have new they met student.
_____

5 haven't dog they found their still.
_____

6 yet hasn't office she at arrived the.
_____

2 Write the past participles of these verbs.

leave	_____	drink	_____
clear	_____	take out	_____
do	_____	put on	_____
go	_____	bring	_____
be	_____	have	_____
draw	_____	find	_____
throw away	_____	tidy	_____

3 Read the telephone conversation and complete it with *already, yet* or *still*.

MARY Hi, Mum. Is everything OK?

MOTHER Oh, hello, Mary. I've had a very busy day. Peter has _____ come. I wasn't expecting him until this evening.

MARY Oh dear. Do you need my help?

MOTHER No, don't worry. If your brother doesn't get in the way, I'll be all right. By the way, have you collected Peter's birthday present _____?

MARY Yes, I've _____ done that. I went to the shop this morning. But I haven't had time to buy his birthday cake _____. I'm _____ at the office and I've _____ got quite a lot to do here.

MOTHER Never mind. I've already prepared the bedrooms. But I haven't started cooking the meal _____; I'm _____ tidying up the dining room. I suppose I can always ask Peter to help.

MARY Poor Mum. I hope the guests don't arrive too early!

MOTHER Come as soon as you finish at the office. Bye for now.

MARY See you later. Bye.

22

4 Read the conversation again. Correct or confirm the statements. Write sentences with *already*, *yet* or *still*.

1 Mary has finished work.
No, she hasn't finished yet. She is still at the office.

2 Mary has bought her brother's birthday cake.

3 She has collected her brother's present.

4 Mary's mother has finished tidying up the dining room.

5 Mary's mother hasn't prepared the bedrooms.

6 She has cooked the meal.

7 Peter is not coming until this evening.

LISTENING

1 Listen to two telephone conversations. Put a tick (✓) if the people know each other or a cross (✗) if they are strangers.

Conversation 1 ☐
Conversation 2 ☐

2 Listen to Conversation 1 again and put a tick (✓) next to the things Henry has already done and a cross (✗) next to the things he hasn't done yet.

1 spoken to Ms Davidson ☐
2 prepared the report ☐
3 sent the report to the hotel ☐
4 posted the mail ☐
5 faxed Mr Brownlee ☐

3 Listen to Conversation 2 again and write full sentences with *already* or *yet*.

1
2
3

SOUNDS

Correct the sentences.

1 He's already done the shopping.
No, he hasn't done it yet.

2 They've already finished the painting.
No,

3 She's already seen the house.
No,

4 They've already bought a new car.
No,

5 He's already tidied up the house.
No,

Listen and repeat the corrected sentences.

WRITING

Look at your Student's Book and write sentences about what you *have already* studied or talked about and what you *haven't done yet*.

1 *non-defining relative clauses*
We have already studied non-defining relative clauses.

2 *the present perfect continuous*

3

4

5

6

VOCABULARY

1 Look at the list of words and the two photos. Match the words with the photos. You can use some words more than once and some words may not be suitable for either of the photos. You can use your dictionary.

avalanche block burn chaos crew currency destroy dollar drown evacuate firefighters forecast freezing gale heat sea helicopter government market official pound rescue sink smoke snow speech storm temperature visit volunteer Wall Street weather wind

Photo A	Photo B
crew	

2 Complete these two news stories with words from 1. You may need to modify nouns and verbs. Which photos do the stories go with?

1 A ship is in difficulty in the North Sea where heavy _____ are making _____ operations extremely dangerous for the _____ crews who have been trying since early this morning to airlift 17 _____ members to safety. One ship crew member has fallen over board and has _____ . It is feared that the ship will _____ before nightfall.

2 The skies are black with thick _____ as the worst fires in 50 years _____ vast areas of forest. Thousands of _____ from neighbouring states have joined the professional _____ and are trying desperately to bring the fires under control. Weather conditions have been making the situation worse: the _____ is 15 degrees above the summer average and there are very high _____ . Police have been _____ people from their homes all day, but some have refused to leave.

GRAMMAR

1 Write sentences in the present perfect continuous with *since* or *for*.

1 I started working at the ministry six years ago. I'm still working there.
I have been working at the ministry for six years.

2 The concert started three hours ago. The band is still playing.

_____

_____

3 The value of the dollar started rising in March. It is still rising.

_____

_____

4   They left Plymouth to sail round the world last June. They are still sailing.

_____

_____

2   Write questions for the sentences in activity 1.

1   *How long have you been working at the ministry?*

2   _____

_____

3   _____

_____

4   _____

_____

5   _____

_____

READING

1   Look quickly at the newspaper articles and match them with these titles. Put the correct letters in the boxes.

1   Airlift saves tortoises from flames ☐

2   Art thieves at work again ☐

3   Russia has flying saucer ☐

2   Read the articles. You can look up five words in your dictionary.

3   Read the articles again and circle the sentences in the present perfect continuous. Underline the time expressions with *for* and *since*.

4   Answer the questions.

1   How long have the Russians been experimenting with flying saucers?

_____

2   How long have soldiers been fighting the fire on the island?

_____

3   How long have the police been trying to trace the missing painting?

_____

SOUNDS

1   Underline the stressed syllables in these words. Say the words aloud.

areas   chaos   evacuate   desperate   destroy rescue   reward   species   volunteer

🔊 Now listen and check.

2   Cross out the silent letters in each of these words. Say the words aloud.

nightfall   neighbouring   know   design   fighting island   weigh

🔊 Now listen and check. Add some more words with silent letters.

A

Russian scientists have built and successfully tested the world's first flying saucer.
The egg-shaped aircraft looks like something out of science fiction. They are now planning a bigger model which will be able to carry 400 people. Aviation experts are taking the idea very seriously because they know that the Russians started experimenting with flying saucer designs many years ago and that they have been testing a saucer for military use for at least a year.

B

Soldiers are desperately fighting a fire that started 13 days ago on the largest of the Galapagos islands. The island is the last home of a rare species of giant tortoise. Helicopters have been lifting tortoises to safety since Monday but the operation is very slow because the animals weigh over 250 kg. The tortoises can live for up to 200 years and it is therefore quite possible that some individuals have been living on the island since 1835 when Charles Darwin, famous for his theory of evolution, visited it.

C

The owners of Edvard Munch's famous painting *The Scream* are offering a reward of more than £720,000 for its return. The painting disappeared from an Oslo gallery last month and there has been no news of it since then. Police are still trying to trace the missing painting.

Fictional heroes never die

VOCABULARY

1 Divide the words in the list into three groups. You can use your dictionary.

appear brave cartoon character comic
conquer delight evil famous fictional film
heroine latest laugh movie novel pet
popular save series successful

Nouns	Adjectives	Verbs
cartoon		

2 Complete the sentences with words from activity 1. You may need to modify verbs.

1 Mickey Mouse _____ in the first Disney _____ in 1928.

2 *Dallas* was a very _____ American television _____ .

3 In his _____ film, which will come out in August, he plays the role of an _____ criminal.

4 Both adults and children _____ at Donald who is probably the funniest and the most _____ duck in the world.

5 *Gone with the Wind* was one of the most _____ movies ever made. It is still popular today. The _____ is a woman called Scarlett O'Hara.

READING

1 The passage consists of two texts about two well-known cartoon characters. The texts have been mixed up. Look quickly at the passage and decide who the two characters are.

2 Read the passage and separate the two texts by underlining the sentences which belong to the same text. The sentences are in the right order.

3 Are you familiar with these characters? Have you read the cartoon books or seen any of the films?

> **What is your favourite cartoon character?**

Hergé, the Belgian cartoonist, died in 1983 but Tintin, his creation, lives on. Asterix the Gaul has conquered most of the world. The brave warrior and his big friend Obelix have been delighting millions of comic-reading children and adults from all over the world for more than 30 years. The brave young reporter made his first big trip on January 10th 1929 to the USSR. Only Americans have so far resisted their charms and the latest film, appropriately called 'Asterix Conquers America', is hoping to do just that. His next trip was to the Congo in 1931 and then to the US in 1932. Since he started his career as a journalist, he has visited more than 30 countries all over the world and has even landed on the moon. 162 million people have seen the six cartoon films, set in Roman times, that have been made to date. He has been solving mysteries and getting out of sticky situations with his faithful dog Snowy for over 60 years.

The cartoon books, set in Roman times, were written and drawn by the French duo of Albert Uderzo and René Goscinny and were first published in the 1960s. He has even appeared in a number of films. The first full-length cartoon of his adventures in Egypt was made in 1969. Since then they have sold more than 200 million copies world-wide and have appeared in over 20 different languages. Since then children and adults from all over the world and speaking over 30 different languages have been following the fantastic adventures of this brave young man.

GRAMMAR

1 Look back at the passage and find three sentences which are in the present perfect continuous.

_____

_____

_____

Find four sentences which are in the present perfect simple.

_____

_____

_____

_____

2 Decide which of the sentences you wrote down in activity 1 describe:

a completed actions

b actions which continue in the present.

3 Put the words in order and write sentences.

1 just from I States arrived the back have.
I have just arrived back from the States

2 have six travelling over I been hours for.

_____

_____

3 more o'clock has he two than cigarettes smoked ten since.

_____

_____

4 to trying been ages give up for has he smoking.

_____

_____

5 new we sports bought red a car have.

_____

_____

6 has in popular appeared two series she television.

_____

_____

4 Complete the sentences with the present perfect continuous or simple.

1 I _____ English for nearly four years now. (study)

2 I _____ all the major tenses. (study)

3 She _____ in Rome since 1986. (live)

4 She _____ in three different flats. (live)

5 They _____ since last year. (act)

6 They _____ in two plays. (act)

7 He _____ on Broadway for the last six months. (appear)

8 He _____ in three popular shows on Broadway. (appear)

5 For which sentences in activity 4 can you ask questions with *how long* and which with *how many*?

Write two questions with each.

1 How long _____

2 How long _____

3 How many _____

4 How many _____

SOUNDS

1 Rewrite the sentences using the contracted form of the verbs. Underline the stressed words.

1 I have been travelling for several weeks.
I've been travelling for several weeks.

2 She has not seen them since last week.

_____

3 They have worked for two different companies.

_____

4 Have you not met my sister Anna?

_____

5 He has not been appearing in the TV series for very long.

_____

6 We have just bought a new house in the suburbs.

_____

2 Listen and say the sentences aloud.

WRITING

Use the notes below to write a paragraph about the fictional character, Donald Duck. You can look at your Student's Book to help you.

created in 1936   hundreds of cartoons   loveable popular   hot-headed   difficult situations

_____

_____

_____

_____

_____

_____

27

VOCABULARY

1 Which of the words below can you use to describe:

1 the buildings and architecture of a town?
   skyscraper
   _____
   _____

2 the atmosphere of a town?
   lively
   _____
   _____

skyscraper noisy romantic bridge concrete
picturesque cathedral landmark lively
fountain exciting square old-fashioned
sophisticated church baroque modern busy
dirty palace sleepy skyline dangerous
industrial wealthy vertical suburb smart low
cosmopolitan gothic town hall tall tower
block glass big

2 Look at the pictures of Naples and Riga. Choose five words to describe each capital from the list above.

Naples _____

Riga _____

GRAMMAR

1 Complete the sentences with the comparative form of the adjectives.

1 Hotels in Naples are _____ than in Lisbon. (cheap)

2 Naples has a _____ population than Riga. (big)

3 In winter, days are _____ in Naples than in Riga. (short)

4 Naples is _____ than Riga. (crowded)

5 Naples is _____ south than Riga. (far)

2 Rewrite these comparative sentences putting Riga first. Change the adjectives so that the meaning is the same.

1 There are more hotels in Naples than in Riga.
   There are fewer hotels in Riga than in Naples.

2 There is less rain in Naples than in Riga.
   _____

3 There are more inhabitants in Naples than in Riga.
   _____

4 Naples is further south than Riga.
   _____

5 There are more tourists in Naples during the summer than in Riga.
   _____

6 Hotels are cheaper in Naples than in Riga.

3 Write five sentences comparing the town where you live with either Riga or Naples.

1 _____
2 _____
3 _____
4 _____
5 _____

SOUNDS

Circle the word with a different vowel sound.

1 sp<u>o</u>t   r<u>o</u>mantic   g<u>o</u>thic   bl<u>o</u>ck
2 sm<u>a</u>rt   gl<u>a</u>ss   h<u>a</u>ll   landm<u>a</u>rk
3 squ<u>a</u>re   p<u>a</u>le   r<u>ai</u>l   m<u>ai</u>n
4 l<u>o</u>w   t<u>o</u>wn   t<u>o</u>wer   f<u>ou</u>ntain
5 b<u>i</u>g   goth<u>i</u>c   b<u>u</u>sy   l<u>i</u>vely

▭ Listen and check.

Icy sun on St Petersburg

As big snowflakes fall silently between the tall trees, the Lazarevskoye cemetery is a magical and lonely scene. It is the final resting place for dozens of Russian artists including Dostoevsky and Tchaikovsky, and an increasingly popular destination for foreign tourists. St Petersburg has many hidden spots like this, that are as good as the over-familiar tourist attractions of the West. The most beautiful time of year for a short break is late January and February when the snow is still on the ground and the misty air is icy cold. St Petersburg is certainly one of the world's grandest winter cities.

The grandiose and colourful architecture, with its surprising blues, greens and pinks, would look tasteless in more southern climates, but here the colours go beautifully with the snow and the pale winter light.

Peter the Great started building the city in 1703. He imported Italian architects to make buildings bigger and better than anywhere else in Europe and much of the city does feel like a Venice for giants. In fact, distances in St Petersburg are so great that it is a good idea to travel by bus or taxi when visiting the city.

In St Petersburg your senses can never rest. You feel, smell and experience life more vividly here than in any other European city. Although the city has been neglected for nearly a century now, its brilliant cultural past is obvious everywhere you go, and its unique beauty charms most visitors.

READING

1 Look quickly at the passage about St Petersburg and decide where it comes from.

– a novel   – an encyclopaedia
– a travel guide   – a letter

2 Read the passage and say if the writer likes St Petersburg.

_____

3 What words does the writer use to describe the following features?

1 the cemetery _____
2 the architecture _____

4 Look back at the passage and underline sentences which make comparisons.

5 Would you say the passage contains:

1 a lot of facts?
2 mostly the writer's impressions?

6 If you were planning to visit St Petersburg, what other information would you be interested in? Make notes.

_____
_____
_____

WRITING

Write a short factual passage about St Petersburg using the information below.

formerly Leningrad   4,900,000 inhabitants
north-west Russia   industrial centre
on the Neva river   scientific research centre
major sea and river port   formerly a cultural centre

_____
_____
_____
_____
_____
_____

I couldn't live without it

VOCABULARY

1 Combine words from Box A with words from Box B to make one-word compound nouns.

A	B
neck	brush
arm	case
brief	tray
spot	lace
wrist	father
sun	light
grand	watch
hair	chair
ash	glasses

2 Circle the odd-word-out in each line.

1 rectangular round pointed square wood
2 rubber cotton short plastic glass
3 interesting old antique modern new
4 hard heavy transparent light soft
5 loose tight long short leather
6 interesting uncomfortable Spanish valuable ugly

GRAMMAR

1 Put the adjectives in the right order.

1 antique/pearl/beautiful necklace
a beautiful antique pearl necklace

2 multi-coloured/silk/expensive carpet

3 set of Venetian/17th-century/magnificent glasses

4 lycra/black/fashionable cycling-suit

5 modern/gold/attractive watch

2 Read the descriptions 1 to 6 below and guess what the objects are. Put the numbers of the descriptions in the correct boxes.

telephone ☐   leather jacket ☐   watch ☐
bicycle ☐   sunglasses ☐   jeans ☐

1 It has an <u>attractive</u> black crocodile strap and an elegant round white face with black Roman numerals set in a delicate white gold case.

2 The popular 1950s design has a square leather label and the well-known round metal rivets which hold on the back pockets.

3 The old-fashioned, heavy black models are not worth buying as collector's pieces, but the valuable Italian Bakelite ones are. Some modern, portable models play a tune while you dial the numbers.

4 It has a well-balanced, light aluminium frame with low, racing handlebars. The wheels and pedals are also made from aluminium and there is a comfortable leather saddle.

5 They have fashionable, yellow rubber frames with amusing, green plastic branches and dark lenses. They are ideal for all outdoor sports.

6 The most expensive design is a comfortable, brown, leather flying model with a real fur collar and authentic military badges on the sleeves and chest.

3 Underline the adjectives in the descriptions which express opinions.

4 Underline the correct possessive pronoun or adjective.

1 *My/mine* car is a Ford. What about *your/yours*?

2 We've left *ours/our* car at the station. What have you done with *your/yours*?

3 This one is *my/mine*, so that one must be *her/hers*.

4 Do you know where *her/hers* keys are? I've only found *my/mine*.

5 Could you pass *my/mine* coat? *Your/yours* is here on the chair.

READING

1 Read this passage about traffic cones and decide if the writer's attitude to cones is positive, negative or neutral.

Design classic: the traffic cone

The traffic cone, everywhere the symbol of traffic jams and road works, is a misunderstood object. Hating it is as irrational as shooting someone who brings you bad news: the cone is only trying to help. Wooden and rubber road cones have existed since the 1950s, but the hollow plastic cone was invented in 1967 by David Morgan, an engineer who was working for ICI at the time. Since then, he has improved the design to make it more stable, more visible, and safer.

Morgan's recipe for the bigger models is to combine an elegant, light top to a heavy recycled-PVC base. The cone must not move too much in wind or from vibration. It is designed to fall apart if a vehicle hits it at speed: the top disintegrates while the heavy base stays safely on the road. Smaller one-piece versions have sand in the base to achieve the same effect.

Morgan makes up to 35,000 cones a week out of the total national production of about 63,000. They cost the buyers between £2 and £7 each, depending on size, and have a surprisingly short life of about two months.

Britain now exports cones: the Irish buy a unique 24-inch green version while Norwegians like theirs to be yellow, to show up in the snow. The Japanese order theirs with flashing lights on top. We in Britain prefer ours to be orange and white. Light, stable, stackable, benevolent, hugely successful – the traffic cone has all the ingredients of a design classic. It is noticeable that nations yet to be conquered by the cone – Germany and France, for instance – have higher rates of road accidents than other countries. Cones are definitely heroes, not gremlins.

2 Are these statements true or false or is there no evidence in the passage?

1 Many people hate traffic cones because they mean that there is likely to be a traffic jam. ☐

2 The cone design has not changed since it was invented in the 1950s. ☐

3 Big cones must be both safe and stable. ☐

4 Only the Irish have green cones. ☐

5 There are more accidents in countries which use cones than in those which don't. ☐

3 Look back at the passage and underline all the adjectives which are used to describe cones.

Find two adjectives which express opinions.

4 Answer the questions and try to guess the meanings of the words or phrases.

1 *symbol*: When there are cones on a road does this mean that (a) the road is clear or (b) there are probably road works?

2 *fall apart*: If a car hits a cone should the cone (a) stay in one piece or (b) break up?

3 *show up*: Which colour cone are you likely to see better in the snow: (a) yellow or (b) white?

4 *yet to be conquered*: Does this mean that cones are (a) not very common or (b) very common in France and Germany?

5 *gremlins*: Is a gremlin likely to be (a) something pleasant or (b) something unpleasant?

WRITING

Write descriptions of the objects in the pictures.

_____
_____
_____
_____
_____
_____
_____
_____
_____
_____

GRAMMAR

1 Look in the *Functions* box of your Student's Book and change the words in italics in these sentences. Do not change the meanings of the sentences.

1   You *are not supposed to* look people in the eyes.

_____

2   In Japan you *should* exchange business cards before starting work.

_____

3   *Are you supposed to* arrive on time at meetings in Latin America?

_____

4   *Should* I offer to pay for the meal?

_____

5   *Do I have to* offer to take business associates home?

_____

2 What is the general attitude to punctuality in these countries? Read the tips from different countries and match these sentences with the countries.

Germany ☐   Spain ☐   France ☐   Britain ☐

1   You should arrive on time for a business meeting, but it's OK to be a little late for social appointments.
2   You mustn't be late.
3   You shouldn't arrive more than 15 minutes late.
4   You don't need to be punctual.

3 Write some advice about punctuality to someone visiting your country.

_____

_____

_____

_____

_____

_____

Germany
It is very important to be punctual, which means on the dot. Keeping others waiting is considered rude.

Spain
Lateness and delay are common in all areas of life and time is considered an artificial framework designed to get people more or less at the same time in the same place.

France
Punctuality depends on the social circumstances and the importance of the person to be kept waiting. About 15 minutes is acceptable.

Britain
People usually arrive on time for business appointments, but it is usually acceptable to arrive up to 10 or 15 minutes after the stated time for a social appointment.

READING

1 Read the passage below and choose the best title.

1   Social behaviour in South Korea
2   The Korean business lunch
3   How to pay your way

If you're invited out for a meal or even just a drinking and dancing session with Korean friends, you'll find it difficult to pay the bill yourself or even contribute to it. The same applies even if it's you that's doing the inviting. All manner of ruses will be used to beat you to the cashier, even if it means that the person who pays is going to have to live on bread and water for the next week. The bill for a group is always paid by one person and one only. If you want to contribute, then make these arrangements before you go out and settle up after you leave. Never attempt to do it in front of the cashier. You will seriously embarrass your host. Indeed, by doing anything like this, you may embarrass them to such a degree that they'll never be able to return to that particular restaurant or club. If you're a man taking a woman out for the night, you pay. She won't even offer.

2 The following sentences are incorrect. Read the passage again and rewrite the sentences.

1 If you are invited out, you should offer to pay for yourself.

_____

_____

2 If you invite people out, it is acceptable to share the cost.

_____

_____

3 The first person to get the bill is supposed to pay.

_____

_____

4 If you are a woman, you should offer to pay for yourself.

_____

_____

LISTENING

1 You are going to hear a woman talking about her experiences of travelling around the world on her own. Write down words or phrases you think she is likely to use.

_____

_____

_____

2 Read this passage, which offers general advice to women travelling alone.

Underline three pieces of advice.

The woman traveller

Strict moral codes make the life of female travellers all over the world more difficult. If you want to avoid trouble, you should pay attention to some unwritten rules.

It is important to accept other countries as they are and to respect their traditions. You shouldn't impose your own cultural behaviour, but instead try to adapt to the customs of the countries you are visiting. In particular, avoid wearing clothes that may shock people from other parts of the world.

3 📼 Now listen to the speaker and decide if she agrees with the advice in the passage.

4 📼 Listen again and underline the points the speaker mentions.

behaviour   eye contact   sunglasses
family   photos   clothes   hair   bare legs
controversial topics   kissing in public

5 What advice can you give to women travellers? Think about the points in activity 4.
You shouldn't behave in an aggressive way.

_____

_____

_____

_____

_____

_____

WRITING

1 Think of two countries that are most likely to be difficult for a woman traveller.

What particular advice can you give for these countries?

_____

_____

_____

_____

_____

_____

2 What advice can you give people visiting your country about the following things?

1 tipping

_____

_____

2 queuing

_____

_____

3 driving

_____

_____

33

17 | *Rose Rose*

GRAMMAR

Read the predictions below. How likely are they to come true? Put them into the correct category.

Certain   *2*

Probable _____

Possible _____

1 She's not likely to arrive on time.
2 I'll definitely see him tomorrow.
3 I may not have time to meet you this evening.
4 She might stay for the weekend if you ask her.
5 I won't go back to the studio this evening.
6 She'll probably be late.
7 Maybe they'll remember to call and see us.
8 He's sure to stay in this evening.

SOUNDS

Disagree with the predictions in *Grammar*. Underline the stressed words.

1   *I'm sure she will arrive on time.*
2 _____
3 _____
4 _____
5 _____
6 _____
7 _____
8 _____

🔊 Listen and check. Say the sentences aloud.

READING

1 You are going to read a short story, *The night express*. Here are some of the words from the story. Check that you understand what they mean.

asleep   cigarette   compartment   corridor
couchette   disturb   go to sleep   light   passenger
pyjamas   quiet   read   smoke   snore   strangle
suitcase   tired   turn off   undress   victim
wake up

Look at the picture and make predictions about the story and what it is about. Write a few sentences.

I'm certain the story will take place in a train.

_____

_____

_____

Now read the story and see if your predictions are correct.

The night express

I found my sleeping compartment five minutes before the train was due to leave. I was lucky – only one other bed was occupied, so I was sure to have a quiet night. My fellow-passenger was already installed in his bunk: only his nose was visible above the blankets.

There was no reply to my 'Good evening', which was a good thing. He must be asleep already, and there was no need to talk. I sat down and began to undress.

'Do you smoke?' I heard from above.

'No, thank you.'

'I can't stand smoke.'

'Don't worry, I don't smoke.'

'But are you sure you are not a smoker and are trying to give it up? You might feel like a cigarette in the middle of the night and you won't be able to help yourself.'

'I've never smoked in my life.'

The voice stopped. I took off a sock.

'But you might start.'

'What?'

'Smoking. Some people start late.'

'I've no such intention. Quite apart from anything else, I've no cigarettes.'

'You might get some from the conductor.'

'We don't even know if he smokes. Anyway, I don't smoke and I'll definitely not start tonight. Good night.'

'You haven't turned off the light.'

'I will, as soon as I'm ready.'

'But you may want to read and I can't sleep with the light on.'

'I can assure you I won't. I'm extremely tired and I only want to get some sleep.'

He stopped as I turned off the light. He sighed and silence fell. I was just falling asleep when I heard the question:

'Do you snore?'

'No.'

'Why not?'

'Because I don't.'

'That's odd. Most people do and I find it disturbing. I have sensitive hearing.'

'I can assure you I won't snore. And now I'd like to go to sleep if you don't mind.'

He let me. I was woken up by a strong light and saw a pointed nose just by my face. He was leaning out of his bunk, pulling at my pyjama sleeve.

'I say. If you don't smoke, and don't snore, and don't leave the lights on, what do you do?'

'You really want to know?'

'Yes. You must be doing something but I don't know what it is. It's making me so anxious, I can't go to sleep.'

'I strangle. Sometimes with my bare hands and sometimes with a rope. Haven't you heard of the notorious Night Express Strangler? He's a pervert and I am that man.'

I spent a quiet night. In the morning I saw him sitting on his suitcase in the corridor. He had sat on the suitcase all night. When he saw me he got up and dragged his suitcase to the other end of the corridor. I felt sorry for him. Life isn't easy for a sensitive man.

2 Look back at the story and underline four things that the stranger thinks his fellow passenger might do.

3 Do you think the man will do these things? Write sentences.

_____

_____

_____

_____

_____

4 Check that you understand the meaning of these adjectives and write their opposites.

tolerant　　　　　*intolerant*_____

patient　　　　　_____

polite　　　　　_____

sensitive　　　　_____

considerate　　　_____

Choose one or more of the adjectives to describe:

the writer _____

the stranger _____

5 Why does the writer say he is the notorious Night Express Strangler? Choose the best statement.

1　He really is a strangler.

2　He's got a good sense of humour.

3　He just said he was so he could sleep.

6 What would you do or say in a similar situation?

_____

_____

_____

WRITING

Write predictions about your future one year, ten years and twenty years from now.

_____

_____

_____

_____

_____

18 What do you do for a living?

VOCABULARY

1 Underline the adjectives in the list below that you can use to describe jobs.

<u>dangerous</u> demanding enjoyable exciting fashionable fun glamorous hard-working independent interesting lively mean patient practical reliable repetitive rewarding sensible sociable sympathetic tiring

2 Which adjectives in the list do you associate with these jobs?

1 doctor   _demanding_
2 judge   _____
3 taxi driver_____
4 interpreter   _____
5 fashion model   _____

SOUNDS

1 Say these words aloud. Underline the /dʒ/ sound.

dangerous enjoyable intelligent judge journalist language manager soldier surgeon

▣ Now listen and check.

2 Say these words aloud. Is the underlined sound /tʃ/ or /ʃ/? Put the words in two groups.

<u>ch</u>ance coa<u>ch</u> effi<u>c</u>ient fa<u>sh</u>ionable profe<u>ss</u>ional pa<u>t</u>ient recep<u>t</u>ionist ri<u>ch</u> Ru<u>ss</u>ian so<u>c</u>iable tea<u>ch</u>er

/tʃ/	/ʃ/

▣ Listen and say the words aloud.

36

READING

1 Look at the pictures of shoes below. Which of these words do you associate with the different shoes?

fashionable ugly young comfortable practical conservative trendy sensible smart fun relaxed cool eccentric boring

Do you wear any of these types of shoes? Are there any that you would never wear?

2 Read the passage and tick (✓) the best title.

1 Choose the best pair
2 Judging men by their shoes
3 Keep up with the fashion

One look at his shoes and you know everything about a man. Is he easygoing or strait-laced? Rich or poor? Messy or fussy? Hip or conservative? The artistic type? Professional? Vice-president or middle management? From the Midwest or California? It's called Shoe Reading.

Comfortable and easy-to-wear. Notice whether they are polished or not. Anyone who is too lazy to bend over and tie his laces must be just as lazy about the rest of his life.

Beware of anyone wearing such neutral footwear, they must be trying to hide something. Or they might just be out running: check the rest of their outfit before you draw your conclusions.

Very fashionable footwear for teenagers. If an adult man wears them they are more than just a fashion statement. He could be a guitar-playing, Bruce Springsteen type: relaxed and cool. Then again he might be just posing as one.

If he wears the kind you buy in health food shops he might be an ageing hippie. He must be one if he's wearing them in mid-winter. Otherwise, check the rest of his outfit to make sure.

If a man wears shoes with little holes on the toes, it is usually a good indication that he can read. He could be a company executive or an old-fashioned doctor, but he must come from a conservative background to be able to wear these.

3 The writer draws conclusions about who men are by looking at their shoes. Underline the phrases in the passage which express these conclusions.

4 Tick (✓) the sentence that best describes the purpose of the passage.

1 To describe different types of men's shoes.

2 To explain how shoes can help you read character.

3 To amuse the reader.

GRAMMAR

1 Draw conclusions using *must* or *can't* and the words in brackets.

1 He drives a very expensive car and owns a private plane. (rich)
He must be very rich.

2 He spends all day walking around the town. (job)

3 They are asking the way to the city centre. (tourists)

4 She works for a daily newspaper. She goes to all the big football matches. (sports reporter)

5 I thought he studied medicine, but he's got an outdoor job now. (doctor)

6 She teaches maths at the university. (stupid)

2 Say what people *could* or *might* do. Choose from the jobs in the list.

teacher   librarian   guide   shop assistant
carpenter   professor   coach driver   nurse
sculptor   manager

1 Fred works with wood.
He could be a carpenter, but might also be a sculptor.

2 Janet works with children.

3 Heather works in a shop.

4 Greg works with tourists.

3 Write two or three sentences about the people in the photos.
She looks very smart and efficient.

He's got a dog so he must like animals.

WRITING

Think of three people you know professionally but not personally. For example, your dentist, a waitress in a café you visit regularly, your hairdresser, a shop assistant.

Write a few sentences describing the sort of people you think they are.

VOCABULARY

1 Which words or phrases do you associate with the following types of holidays? Choose from the list below. You can use your dictionary.

adventure holiday   package tour   luxury holiday

backpack camping canoe charter flight
characterless cheap coach trip comfort cruise
dangerous economical elegance excitement
expedition expensive first class guided tour
hitchhike horseback hospitality hotel suite
independence package practical remote places
resort sightseeing souvenirs swimming pool
unusual   weekend break

2 Complete the sentences with words or phrases from the list above.

1 Independent travellers often avoid
   _____ holidays because they
   dislike the group image of this type of travel.

2 Sightseeing can be more interesting if you go
   on a _____ .

3 Sightseeing tours are often in the most popular
   areas and usually do not take you to
   _____ .

4 When you hitchhike it is easier to carry your
   belongings in a _____ rather than
   in a suitcase.

5 When you go on a package holiday you are
   likely to travel on a _____ .

6 If you want comfort and good service, you
   should travel _____ .

7 Many people buy _____ to take
   home with them.

FUNCTIONS

1 Do these sentences mean the same? Put a tick (✓) if they are the same and a cross (✗) if they are different.

1 You are allowed to hitch-hike on the
   motorway.
   You are supposed to hitch-hike on the
   motorway. ☐

2 You are not supposed to take your
   shoes off.
   You are obliged to take your shoes off. ☐

3 Christians are not allowed to marry
   Muslim women.
   Christians can't marry Muslim women. ☐

4 She was obliged to show her passport.
   She had to show her passport. ☐

5 You don't have to visit the cathedral in
   the morning.
   You are not supposed to visit the
   cathedral in the morning. ☐

2 Write two rules for each of the following places. Use expressions from the *Functions* box in your Student's Book.

1 cathedral
   You are not supposed to run about.
   You are not allowed to shout.

2 plane
   _____
   _____

3 art museum
   _____
   _____

4 train
   _____
   _____

READING

1 Read *The trouble with photography* and decide if the passage is from:

1 a description of the writer's experiences

2 a traveller's guide to photography

I have been in jail three times in my life and in each case the cause was photography. I had pointed my camera in the wrong direction at the wrong time. Great difficulties can be created quite unintentionally and with the most innocent of motives. So, if you want to avoid trouble you should always find out exactly what restrictions there are. And stick to them. In many places now you are obliged to obtain a photographic permit. Make sure you get one. It is no guarantee against trouble, but it may help. You have to show it to frontier officials when leaving the country, and if you don't have one your camera and films may be confiscated.

As a general rule, in most countries of the world you are not allowed to take photographs of military installations, troop movements or airfields. In some places you are not even supposed to photograph examples of civil engineering – scenes that make the country look primitive – industrial plants, trains, bridges, etc.

Watch out for religious or cultural prohibitions. This can result in violence against you. In some Islamic countries you can't photograph women at all. Whereas you are usually allowed to photograph the exterior of mosques, you are rarely allowed to photograph the interior of the buildings or the people at worship.

You have to be especially careful in remote areas where people are less accustomed to tourists and can be deeply offended by their behaviour. In China, for example, you are allowed to photograph ancient monuments and religious temples quite freely and you don't usually need to ask for permission, but in the remoter Tibetan temples photography is prohibited and you may have your film destroyed if you are not careful.

You should always ask for permission if you want to photograph people. Respect their dignity and right of privacy. In some countries, such as Kenya, you usually have to pay people if you want them to pose for you. One good way of persuading reluctant subjects to pose is to carry a Polaroid camera. Take one shot and let them have it. Then shoot your main pictures. But you should save this tactic for an emergency because Polaroid film is very expensive.

The trouble with photography

2 Answer the questions and try to guess the meanings of the words or phrases.

1 *stick to them*: Should you ignore the restrictions or keep to them?

2 *no guarantee*: If you are careful about the restrictions, are you sure to avoid trouble?

3 *confiscated*: Are they likely to let you keep your film or take it away from you?

4 *remote areas*: Are these popular tourist places or places that are far from the big centres?

5 *offended*: Are they likely to approve or disapprove of the tourists' behaviour?

6 *natives*: Are they people who live in the country or tourists?

3 Write down three things that, according to the passage, you are:

1 not allowed to photograph

military installations
_____

2 obliged to do

_____

3 allowed to photograph

_____

4 not supposed to photograph

_____

_____

4 Are there any photography restrictions in your country?

_____

_____

In what countries are restrictions the strictest?

_____

_____

WRITING

Write a paragraph telling a visitor to a National Park about the park regulations.

Think about the following:

dogs flowers camping paths wildlife fires
guns radios guides permission

_____

_____

_____

_____

_____

_____

20 | *How unfair can you get?*

VOCABULARY

1 Combine words from Box A with words from Box B to form compound adjectives.

A	B
bad	aged
cool	assured
easy	behaved
fair	famous
good	fashioned
hard	going
middle	handed
old	headed
right	hearted
self	mannered
short	minded
soft	sighted
world	tempered
well	working

bad-mannered

_____

_____

_____

_____

_____

_____

_____

2 Complete the sentences with compound adjectives from your list in activity 1.

1 Someone who is not polite is _____ .

2 Someone who does not panic easily is

_____ .

3 Someone who works a lot is _____ .

4 Someone who does not have modern taste is

_____ .

5 Someone who is well known in many

countries is _____ .

GRAMMAR

1 Complete the sentences with *could* or *was/were able to*.

1 He was very aggressive but I _____
keep calm.

2 When she was young, she _____ dance
quite well.

3 There weren't many people when I arrived, so I
_____ get a seat by the window.

4 Everyone liked him because he _____
always see both sides of an argument.

5 I _____ relax with them because they
weren't at all prejudiced.

2 Which sentences in activity 1 refer to:

1 a general ability in the past?

_____

2 a specific occasion in the past?

_____

3 Write sentences with *could* or *was/were able to*.

1 I was angry but _____

_____

2 The restaurant was full but _____

_____

3 When he was young, he _____

_____

4 He was good-natured and _____

_____

5 It was a lovely day so _____

_____

4 Complete the sentences with *can, could* or the correct form of *be able to*. Sometimes more than one answer is possible.

1 They told him where the hotel was but he still _____ find it.

2 I used to _____ play football quite well.

3 It was so funny she _____ stay serious.

4 I hope you _____ find a decent hotel.

5 When you have time, perhaps you _____ read this report.

6 They _____ discuss a lot of important things since they arrived.

7 When I am in a stressful situation I _____ usually keep calm.

8 The weather was terrible so she _____ play tennis.

5 Which sentences in activity 4 can you rewrite using *manage to*?

_____

6 Write sentences using *be able to*.

1 When I get home, I _____

_____

2 I was so angry, I _____

_____

3 When we are in Prague, I hope we _____

_____

4 It has been snowing heavily for a week so we

_____

5 They arrived late but they _____

_____

WRITING

1 Write about four English grammar points you can use now you have finished this lesson.

I use 'can' or 'can't' to talk about general _____

ability. _____

_____

_____

_____

2 Write about personal qualities you had or didn't have as a teenager.

When I was a teenager I couldn't understand _____

my parents. _____

_____

_____

_____

_____

VOCABULARY

1 Find 20 adjectives in the puzzle. They go in two directions [➡] and [⬇]. Some letters may be used more than once.

```
B  O  R  I  N  G  S  A  F  E
R  E  M  A  R  K  A  B  L  E
I  X  B  A  D  D  E  N  S  E
L  C  U  F  L  S  G  D  U  N
L  I  N  A  I  L  O  U  D  T
I  T  U  S  V  O  O  L  D  I
A  I  S  T  E  W  D  L  E  R
N  N  U  F  U  N  N  Y  N  E
T  G  A  W  K  W  A  R  D  Z
D  E  L  I  G  H  T  F  U  L
```

2 Complete the sentences with adverbs formed from adjectives in the puzzle.

1 He shouted so _____ that everyone heard him.

2 The main character acted so _____ that people walked out.

3 She was driving too _____ when the policeman stopped her.

4 'It was _____ his fault; I wasn't even there at the time.'

5 She is extremely clever and she passed the test _____ .

6 We were very relieved when they finally got back _____ .

7 They _____ appeared round the corner.

8 I understand English very _____ now.

GRAMMAR

1 Make adverbs from these adjectives.

absolute   *absolutely*
awful   _____
beautiful   _____
emotional   _____
exceptional   _____
extreme   _____
fantastic   _____
outstanding   _____
particular   _____
simple   _____
real   _____
terrible   _____

2 Choose suitable adverbs from the list above to emphasise the opinions expressed in these sentences. More than one adverb may be suitable.

1 We ate at a good restaurant last night.
We ate at an exceptionally good restaurant last night.

2 She was wearing an elegant outfit.
_____

3 I watched a fascinating TV programme.
_____

4 The music was delightful.
_____

5 The special effects were far-fetched.
_____

6 The play was depressing.
_____

LISTENING

1 🔲 Listen to two people talking about a film called *Four Weddings and a Funeral*. Have they both seen the film? What type of film is it?

2 🔲 Listen again and complete the sentences with the adjectives and adverbs the speakers use.

1 We saw a _____ _____ film.

2 Hugh Grant plays Charles, an _____ _____ young gentleman.

3 Carrie is a _____ _____ American woman.

4 There is a whole cast of _____ _____ actors.

5 The first wedding scene is _____ _____ .

6 The funeral scene is _____ _____ .

7 The ending is _____ _____ .

SOUNDS

1 Underline the stressed syllables.

absolutely amazingly especially extraordinarily extremely incredibly particularly really remarkably terribly

🔲 Listen and check. Say the words aloud.

2 🔲 Listen and underline the words the speaker stresses. Say the sentences aloud.

1 It's an extremely good film.

2 The acting is really brilliant.

3 The special effects are absolutely extraordinary.

4 The opening scene is terribly funny.

5 The plot is remarkably simple.

6 The ending is completely unexpected.

READING

1 The passage describes the plot of a well-known film classic. Read the passage and decide which of these opinions matches the film.

1 It was the funniest film I've ever seen. ☐

2 I've never seen such a happy ending. ☐

3 It was terribly frightening. ☐

4 I thought the story was really delightful. ☐

The Birds, by Alfred Hitchcock, is a brilliant film of gripping suspense. Melanie Daniels, played by Tippi Hedren, is buying a parrot when Mitch, an extremely good-looking lawyer played by Rod Taylor, enters the shop and plays a practical joke on the young woman. To revenge herself she decides to send him a pair of love birds. She goes to his address and discovers that he is away for the weekend. So she drives to Bogata Bay where he is staying with his mother and sister. She crosses the bay in a boat and discreetly leaves the cage at the house. But as she is climbing out of the boat, a seabird violently attacks her and Mitch comes to her rescue. The following day the birds kill a man and from then on terror reigns in the village where the attacks are increasingly vicious and frequent. Mitch and Melanie barricade themselves in the house and frantically fight off the birds which seem determined to kill. The couple finally manage to escape from the house with the mother and sister who carries the love birds. The ending is ambiguous because when they are driving away, the village is still under attack. The audience leaves the cinema with an uneasy feeling.

2 Answer these questions.

1 What's the title of the film? _____

2 Who directed it? _____

3 What type of film is it? _____

4 Who are the main actors? _____

5 Have you seen it? _____

3 Underline six adverbs in the passage. What adjectives or verbs do they modify?

WRITING

Write a paragraph about a book you have read recently. Include these points:

the title   the type of book   the plot

why you like it   your favourite character

_____

_____

_____

_____

_____

_____

VOCABULARY

Complete the crossword.

Across:
1 The largest sea mammal.
5 A very big bird.
7 An animal that lives in the polar regions.
8 Hunt animals illegally.
10 Most birds can do this.
11 A domestic pet.
12 It looks a bit like a dog.

Down:
1 Not a pet animal.
2 A big African cat.
3 An Indian beauty.
4 Many _____ of animal are already extinct.
5 The biggest land mammal.
6 Hunters kill elephants for this.
9 A frightening dog-like animal.

GRAMMAR

1 Are these adverbs and adverb phrases of manner, place or time? Put them in the correct columns.

slowly   last year   in the wild
all over the country   by car   soon   suddenly
in Asia   in the mountains   in 1965   sharply
at first   then   there   on foot   finally   gradually
everywhere   ten years ago   in the west   officially

manner	place	time
slowly		

2 Underline the adverb phrases in the sentences. Are they adverb phrases of time, manner or place?

1 The lion got up and walked away slowly. *manner* .
2 Poachers have already killed thousands of rhinos this year. _____.
3 She came back suddenly last week. _____.
4 In the mountains most people travel on foot. _____.
5 In the 1960s the eagle was in danger of becoming extinct. _____.
6 In Europe today it is illegal to hunt many animals. _____.

3 Read the sentences and decide where these adverb phrases can go. There may be more than one possibility.

1 Humans killed animals for food and clothing. (thousands of years ago)
2 Many species have disappeared. (completely)
3 There are laws that protect some animals. (today)
4 But many poachers still shoot animals. (illegally)
5 People have reintroduced animals. (in some places)
6 For instance, naturalists have reintroduced lynx. (in Switzerland)

4 Complete the sentences with your own answers.

1 Suddenly he _____
2 Last year I _____
3 All over the world _____
4 In my country _____
5 Today _____
6 In the end _____
7 Slowly _____

5 Write sentences using the adverb phrases in brackets.

1 (on foot) *I always go to work on foot.*

2 (by car) _____

3 (carefully) _____

4 (in the last few years) _____

5 (in my country) _____

READING

1 The passages are about two animal species. Read them and find out what the two species are and what they have in common. Tick (✓) the correct statements.

1 They are both birds. ☐

2 They are both in danger of extinction. ☐

3 They are both national symbols. ☐

4 They are both rare because humans have hunted them mercilessly. ☐

5 Most people have only seen the animals in zoos. ☐

2 Read passage A again and underline all the adverbs and adverbial phrases.

3 Read passage B again and decide where these adverbs or adverbial phrases can go.

a in the wild   b 30 years ago

c all over the United States   d officially   e rapidly

4 Complete the titles of the passages with a suitable adverb of manner.

suddenly   majestically   illegally   gradually
immediately

A: Kiwi moves _____ towards extinction

B: American eagle flies _____ out of danger's reach

5 Does your country have an animal as its national symbol? If not, which animal would you choose?

_____

_____

_____

_____

A The shy, flightless kiwi, which is New Zealand's national symbol, is heading gradually towards extinction. Sadly, this year all three species of kiwi will go on the endangered species list. A recent survey shows that kiwis are disappearing rapidly from the forests where they have lived for thousands of years.

Ten years ago conservationists thought that the kiwi's future was secure. But today they warn that if the government does not act immediately, the kiwi may disappear completely in less than ten years.

Dogs, cats and Australian possums are rapidly reducing the numbers of this discreet, nocturnal bird. Humans introduced these animals into New Zealand where no mammals lived until modern times. In the past there were probably millions of kiwis living in the vast forests. Their only predator was the large New Zealand eagle, which itself became extinct thousands of years ago.

Zoos in New Zealand have several birds and these are the only ones which most humans are ever likely to see. It would be extremely unfortunate if the national emblem of the country went the same way as its great eagle.

B The majestic bald eagle has made an astonishing recovery. America's patriotic mascot was close to extinction (1) _____ (when). The government will (2) _____ (how) remove it from the country's list of endangered species this year.

The government declared the bald eagle to be the national symbol in 1782. But farmers felt little affection for the predator and they killed thousands of birds at the beginning of this century.

The eagle was once a common sight (3) _____ (where). But chemical pesticides, deforestation and hunters reduced the number of birds to just 400 pairs in the early 1960s. The bald eagle became so rare that most Americans have only ever seen their national symbol in zoos or on the back of dollar bills.

In the 1960s the government banned the insecticide DDT and it became illegal to hunt the bird. The number of eagles increased (4) _____ (how). Today more than 8,000 bald eagles live (5) _____ (where) in the United States.

23 | Valentine

VOCABULARY

1 Write one or two words which you associate with each of the words in the list below. You can use your dictionary to help you.

grief _____

jealousy _____

love _____

marriage _____

passion _____

separation _____

romance _____

trust _____

2 Match each of the words in Box A with a word in Box B which has a similar meaning. You can use your dictionary.

A	B
happy	suspicious
faithful	truthful
jealous	intense
honest	true
selfish	content
cruel	unhappy
passionate	mean
sad	unkind

3 Write the nouns formed from the adjectives in Box A above.

happy   happiness

_____   _____

_____   _____

_____   _____

_____   _____

GRAMMAR

1 Rewrite these sentences in reported speech.

1 'I've fallen in love with a beautiful girl,' he said.
   He said he had fallen in love with a beautiful girl.

2 'I sent her a Valentine card,' he said.
   _____

3 'I love her,' he said.
   _____

4 'I'm the happiest man in the world,' he said.
   _____

5 'I've bought her a diamond ring,' he said.
   _____

6 'I'm getting married on Saturday,' he said.
   _____

2 Rewrite the sentences in reported speech. Change the time reference.

1 'I'm going next week,' he said.
   He said he was going the following week.

2 'We'll see you tomorrow,' she said.
   _____

3 'I came back from London three weeks ago,' she said.
   _____

4 'We got home late last night,' they said.
   _____

5 'I'm staying at home today,' she said.
   _____

6 'I'm not going out tonight,' he said.
   _____

SOUNDS

1 🔊 Listen to these words. Which ones contain the sounds /ʃ/, /s/ or /z/ ? Put them in three columns.

passionate   fierce   selfish   shrink   sure   rose
satin   kiss   suspicious   scent   possessive
always   doesn't   reflection

/ʃ/	/s/	/z/
passionate	*selfish*	
selfish		

Now say the words aloud.

2 Match the words with the same vowel sound.

1   truth   ☐ Valentine
2   tears   ☐ card
3   heart   ☐ lips
4   ring   ☐ feel
5   blind   ☐ fierce
6   grief   ☐ loop

🔊 Now listen and check. Say the words aloud.

READING

1 Read *A warm relationship*, a mini-story about a relationship, and decide which of these sentences are true.

1   The man loves the woman.   ☐
2   The woman loves the man.   ☐
3   The woman loves money.   ☐
4   They love each other.   ☐

A warm relationship

'I'm cold,' she said.
She shivered and held
herself tightly.
'My love will keep you warm,'
he said with enthusiasm.
She tried his love.
'I'm still cold,' she said.
'You can have this money,'
he said, disappointed.
'You can buy yourself a fur coat.'
She smiled and warmed with a
shiver of anticipation.

2 Rewrite these sentences in reported speech.

1   'I'm cold,' she said.

_____

_____

2   'My love will keep you warm,' he said.

_____

3   'I'm still cold,' she said.

_____

_____

4   'You can have this money,' he said.

_____

_____

5   'You can buy yourself a fur coat,' he said.

_____

_____

3 Which of the words below would you choose to describe the following things?

1   the man's attitude towards the woman?
2   the woman's attitude towards the man?
3   the title of the story?

cynical   faithful   ironic   passionate   honest
weak   resigned   jealous   dishonest

VOCABULARY

1 Underline the words in the list below that you can use to talk about television. What would you use the other words to talk about?

serial edition screen print remote control headlines viewers glossy publish episode tabloid programme show readers series channel media circulation audience

2 Complete the sentences with words from the list. You may have to change the form of some of the nouns.

1 In India, sports _____ are almost as popular as serials.

2 British children spend, on average, 13 hours a week in front of the television _____ .

3 You use a _____ to change channels.

4 If you want to read serious political articles you would not buy a British _____ paper.

5 In some countries the government controls the _____ .

READING

1 Read the passage about Egyptian television and match the headings with the paragraphs.

1 The nights of Ramadan ☐

2 American soaps ☐

3 Serials that bring a nation to a standstill ☐

4 Television and the rest of the media ☐

2 Answer the questions and try to guess the meaning of these words or expressions.

1 *powerful hold*: Does television influence people's lives a lot or not very much?

2 *dominated*: Are there a lot of these shows on television or not very many?

3 *glued to*: Are they likely to watch the whole serial carefully or just parts of it?

4 *time on their hands*: Does this mean they are very busy or they have a lot of free time?

5 *binge*: Do they watch a lot of television or less television during this month?

A Here in Egypt, television has a powerful hold over people's minds. It is an instrument of leisure, of information and – to a very limited extent – of culture. It does not stop people reading newspapers or books, going to the cinema or theatre or watching videos. But these activities are occasional, irregular and ultimately of secondary importance. Television is one of the main subjects of conversation, at school, in offices, at home and in the street, as well as being written about in all the newspapers.

B It might be said that the main objective of television is to persuade the maximum number of people to watch it for the maximum amount of time. And how effectively the sitcoms and soap operas do that! I do not think that I have ever seen any other country so totally dominated by these shows. Some of them are Egyptian productions but the majority are American. Each episode, each programme, is a talking point for everyone, young and old alike.

C It is therefore not surprising that an extraordinary ritual takes place when it is time for a serial to begin. All the members of the family stop whatever they have been doing and sit glued to the screen. The ritual is not confined to those with time on their hands. If you want to leave the free-trade zone in Port Said while a serial is on, then forget it. You won't be able to get through customs until the end of the episode.

D Ramadan, the month of fasting, is the month in which television reigns supreme. This is partly because people have more time on their hands than during the rest of the year, but also because cinemas and theatres close down and other public cultural activities come to a halt. During Ramadan people go on a kind of television binge. Besides the normal shows, special serials running from the first to the last day of the month are produced each year and are eagerly awaited by millions of viewers.

3 These statements are false. Find out what the passage really says and rewrite the statements.

1 Television is an important instrument of culture.

_____

_____

2 Egyptians watch as much television as people from any other countries.

_____

_____

3 The sitcoms and soap operas are mostly Egyptian productions.

_____

_____

4 These shows attract mainly the younger viewers.

_____

_____

5 Only serials are broadcast on television during Ramadan.

_____

_____

LISTENING

1 [cassette] Listen to two people talking about television. Put a tick (✓) by the types of programmes they mention.

cartoon   documentary   sports   soap opera
the news   quiz show   film   sitcom

2 [cassette] Listen again and put the questions the speakers ask in the correct order. Write the number of the question in the box.

☐ a Was it an exciting match?

☐ b What are you doing this evening?

☐ c Did they show the finals of the men's tennis?

☐ d What channel's it on?

☐ e What was the second episode like?

☐ f Who won?

☐ g Do you want me to record the documentary for you?

☐ h Did you watch the sport last night?

GRAMMAR

1 Turn the direct questions in *Listening* activity 2 into reported questions.

1 She asked *if the match had been exciting.*

2 She asked _____

3 She asked _____

4 He asked _____

5 He asked _____

6 She asked _____

7 She asked _____

8 He asked _____

2 Turn these reported questions into direct questions. Use *you*.

1 He asked if she had enjoyed the last episode.
'Did you enjoy the last episode?' he asked.

2 She asked if he was going to the cinema.

_____

3 He asked if she was interested in sport.

_____

4 She asked why he didn't watch the soap.

_____

5 He asked if she preferred the news on the radio or the television.

_____

6 She asked if he could record a movie.

_____

WRITING

Write a paragraph describing what you like or dislike about television in your country.

_____

_____

_____

_____

_____

_____

_____

_____

_____

_____

25 | *A cup of tea*

GRAMMAR

1 Match the two parts of the sentences.

1	She promised	a	her they would be late.
2	They offered	b	the drink politely.
3	He warned	c	her son she would take him to the park.
4	He explained	d	him a new job.
5	She refused	e	why they were late.

2 Rewrite the sentences above in direct speech. There may be more than one answer.

1 _____

2 _____

3 _____

4 _____

5 _____

READING

1 Read part 1 of the story *The dead of night* and put these sentences in the right order. Number them 1 to 6.

☐ a The doctor asked one of the men to move into the spare room.

☐ b Mr Wallis reluctantly agreed to move.

☐ c They decided to put a bed in the spare room.

☐ d The doctor explained that they had died because they were terminally ill.

☐ e He persuaded Mr Wallis to move into the spare room.

☐ f Mr Langley warned them that all the patients who had slept there had died.

The dead of night

We were short of space so we installed an old bed from the store in the spare room as a temporary measure. The first person to sleep in that bed was old Mr Bevan. He was terminally ill and he died in his sleep the first night.

We had a ward of three elderly men, Mr Langley, Mr Howell and Mr Wallis. They had almost recovered and were due to leave. I needed an extra bed so I asked if one of them would move into the side room. Mr Langley pointed out that anyone who went into the side ward came out feet first. There had been one other person since Mr Bevan. I said: 'Of course, that's because we put the terminal cases in there. We need a bed badly so one of you will have to go.' Reluctantly, Mr Wallis said he would.

2 Underline the objects of the reporting verbs in the sentences in activity 1.

Now look at the patterns for reporting verbs in the *Grammar* box of your Student's Book. Decide what patterns the sentences belong to.

Sentence a *Pattern 2*   Sentence d _____

Sentence b _____   Sentence e _____

Sentence c _____   Sentence f _____

3 Read part 2 of the story and complete these sentences using the words in brackets.

1 Mr Langley asked _____ (the doctor, why)

2 The doctor admitted _____ (not know)

3 Mr Langley reminded _____ (doctor, Mr Wallis, fine)

4 He warned _____ (the bed)

5 The doctor tried to persuade _____ (Mr Langley, spare room)

6 Mr Langley refused _____ (spare room)

My beeper went off at midnight: cardiac arrest. When I got there they were giving Mr Wallis electric shocks but they gave up after fifteen minutes.

Next morning I went to see Mr Langley and Mr Howell. 'So how do you explain it?' Mr Langley said.

'I don't know. It could happen to anyone.'

'He was fine when he was with us. There's something about that old bed,' he said.

I said the bed was fine. And so was the room. It was just one of those things.

That weekend there were a lot of admissions and we needed a spare bed.

As Mr Langley was almost well I asked him if he'd spend a couple of nights there.

He said, 'You must be joking.'

'It's just a couple of nights till we move some of these new people.'

'Listen, doc,' he said. 'There have been three people in there since I've been here and they've all died. It gives me the creeps.'

I said, 'I told you it was because we use it for terminal cases, it's a perfectly good bed.'

'What about Mr Wallis – he wasn't terminal.'

'That was just bad luck.'

4 Here are some extracts from the next part of the story. Rewrite them in reported speech using a suitable reporting verb.

1 'Yeah, well you can forget about shifting me in there because I'm not moving.'

_____

_____

2 'I'd rather sleep in the toilet.'

_____

_____

3 'Can you come and see Mr Howell.'

_____

_____

4 'He's fine, just a little upset.'

_____

_____

5 Read part 3 of the story.

'Yeah, well you can forget about shifting me in there because I'm not moving.'

'Listen, you're as fit as a flea. You're the obvious person to move.'

'Honest, doc,' he said. 'I'd rather sleep in the toilet.'

So we moved Mr Howell instead. He was there for four days. Then one night my beeper went off at three in the morning. It was the night sister.

'Can you come and see Mr Howell.'

'Is he all right?' I asked.

'He's fine, just a little upset.'

I found him sitting in bed. He'd had a nightmare, he said, in which the blankets had tightened around him and were squeezing the air out of him. He had called the nurse in panic. He felt fine now. I examined him thoroughly. Everything was normal. He'd just had a nightmare.

WRITING

1 Can you guess what happens next? Complete the paragraph.

I was off that weekend. When I came back...

_____

_____

_____

Turn to page 90 and see if you were right.

2 Write the story from Mr Langley's point of view.

_____

_____

_____

_____

_____

_____

_____

_____

_____

_____

_____

_____

_____

_____

_____

_____

_____

Eat your heart out ... in the USA

READING

1 Read the passage *Some rattlin' good recipes* and find out what the recipes are made with and which country they come from.

Some rattlin' good recipes

Fang Casserole, Snappin' Spaghetti and Potted Poison could soon be on the menus of Europe's restaurants.

'For a century or more, rattlesnakes have provided sporting entertainment and innumerable meals for Americans,' said Peppy Wenglarz, a veteran venomous reptile hunter from Arkansas who lost three fingers after a bite.

He leads a group of American hunters who are responsible for the publication of the world's first rattlesnake cook-book. They are now getting the feel of their next market, Europe, where they hope to make inroads this year.

They are confident that the French will soon develop a taste for the exotic meat, as a well-cooked rattler tastes very much like a frog. The gourmet rattler recipe book contains tips for preparing dishes such as Snake Chowder, Snake Bake, Boiled Snake Tails, Pit Viper Jambalaya and Okeene Snake Chilli, which involves throwing in a live rattlesnake to give it that extra bit of bite. 'It's an acquired taste, a delicacy,' said Wenglarz. 'After the success in Europe of other strange meats, such as alligator, kangaroo and ostrich, we think this could be the next thing for the fashionable person who has eaten everything.'

2 Write down the words from the passage you can use to talk about food.

_____

_____

_____

3 Underline three meats in the passage which the writer describes as *strange*.

4 Would you try any of these recipes or strange meats? Do you eat anything in your country which foreigners might consider strange?

_____

_____

_____

_____

VOCABULARY

1 Find 20 verbs in the puzzle. They go in two directions [➡] and [⬇]. Use each letter once only.

S	P	R	E	A	D	F	R	Y
B	P	E	E	L	C	H	O	P
A	P	M	I	X	H	E	A	T
K	O	R	G	S	L	I	C	E
E	U	O	R	S	E	R	V	E
B	R	A	I	P	O	A	C	S
O	C	S	L	U	I	D	O	O
I	U	T	L	T	L	D	O	A
L	T	T	A	S	T	E	L	K

2 Complete the recipe below with verbs from the puzzle.

Tropical salad with alligator

Mix _____ oil, vinegar, garlic and spices to make a marinade.

1 _____ alligator tail meat in marinade for 24 hours.

2 _____ in fridge for one hour.

3 _____ the alligator tail very finely.

4 _____ chopped walnut, pine nuts, ginger and lettuce.

5 _____ the lettuce mixture on a plate.

6 _____ the meat in the centre.

7 _____ some left-over marinade into a pan.

8 _____ half a white cabbage finely.

9 _____ bean sprouts and mango.

10 _____ these ingredients quickly on a high gas and add to lettuce mixture. Serve immediately.

LISTENING

1 You are going to hear three people giving instructions and special advice for preparing different dishes. Write down the ingredients you would use to make these dishes.

a chocolate cake _____

_____

hamburgers _____

_____

a mixed salad _____

_____

2 🔲 Listen and write the number of the speaker by the dish they describe.

☐ a chocolate cake   ☐ hamburgers

☐ a mixed salad

3 Match the instructions below with the speakers.

Speaker 1 | *c* | ☐ | ☐
Speaker 2 | ☐ | ☐ | ☐ | ☐
Speaker 3 | ☐ | ☐ | ☐

a Toss the salad.
b Put the chocolate in a pan.
c Add tomato ketchup.
d Open the walnuts.
e Mix the butter and sugar.
f Serve with chips.
g Cut the avocado in half.
h Add the flour.
i Take the skin off.
j Grill the burgers.
k Beat in the eggs.

🔲 Listen again and check.

GRAMMAR

1 Give special advice for the recipes. Write sentences with *never* or *always*.

1 Put the bread rolls in a hot oven.
   Never put bread rolls in a very hot oven.

2 Dry the lettuce well.

   _____

3 Boil the chocolate.

   _____

4 Use olive oil with walnuts.

   _____

5 Add lemon juice to avocados.

   _____

2 Give special advice with *make sure* and *don't forget*.

1 oven, too hot
   Make sure the oven is not too hot.

2 oil, baking tin

   _____

3 oven on to heat

   _____

4 add spoonful of flour

   _____

5 mixture is creamy

   _____

WRITING

1 Write the instructions for your favourite recipe. Include details of ingredients and any useful tips.

_____

_____

_____

_____

2 Write instructions and give special advice for one of these activities.

playing tennis   laying the table

getting money out of a cash machine

_____

_____

_____

_____

_____

_____

_____

_____

_____

_____

Home thoughts from abroad

VOCABULARY

1 Complete the sentences with *who, which/that* or *where.*

1 It is a boat _____ transports people and vehicles. _____

2 He or she is someone _____ stays in a hotel. _____

3 It is an area _____ there is not much green space. _____

4 It is a boat _____ has hit rocks and sunk. _____

5 It is a document _____ you need to enter some countries. _____

6 It is a place _____ you can spend a holiday. _____

7 He or she is someone _____ decorates houses. _____

8 It is land _____ is surrounded by water. _____

2 Now match the definitions in activity 1 with these people, things or places. Write the correct answer by each definition.

built-up area   crowded place   ferry   guest
guide   hotel   interior designer   island   snow
swimming pool   telegram   visa   waiter   wreck

GRAMMAR

1 Complete the sentences with *which/that, who, where* or *whose.*

1 These are the photos _____ we took of Corsica.

2 There's a café on the corner _____ you can get a really good meal.

3 The hotel _____ we stayed was on the seafront.

4 This is the man _____ we met on the island.

5 She's the person _____ restaurant is in the mountains.

6 Here is the bathing costume _____ I bought on holiday.

7 The town _____ we liked best was up in the mountains.

8 The couple _____ boat we borrowed have gone away for the weekend.

2 Which of the sentences in activity 1 can you rewrite leaving out the relative pronoun?

📼 Listen and check.

3 Complete the sentences with the information in brackets. Leave out the relative pronoun where possible.

1 What's the name of the hotel
   you're staying at _____ ?
   (You're staying at a hotel.)

2 Was the museum _____
   interesting?
   (You visited a museum this morning.)

3 Was the map _____
   very useful?
   (You bought a map at the station.)

4 There weren't many people on the beach
   _____.
   (You told us about a beach.)

5 Have you met the couple
   _____ ?
   (There is a young couple sitting by the window.)

6 I showed her the photos
   _____ .
   (I took photos of Paris.)

7 Did you find the restaurant
   _____ ?
   (I recommended a restaurant to you.)

8 Have you ever been back to the Greek island
   _____ ?
   (You met your husband on a Greek island.)

SOUNDS

📼 Write the relative pronoun you hear: *which*, *that*, or put – if there is no relative pronoun.

1 The man _____ came yesterday is the owner of the boat.

2 I showed her the photos _____ I took of the village.

3 There's the house _____ we rented last summer.

4 The nicest place _____ we've been to is Prague.

5 It's a thing _____ is useful in the kitchen.

6 We're looking after a dog _____ belongs to our friends.

📼 Listen again and check. Say the sentences aloud.

READING

1 The passages are about two people's holiday experiences. Read them and find out if the writers enjoyed their holidays.

2 Look back at the passages and underline the adjectives the writers use to describe their experiences.

3 Find any sentences in the passages where you can insert *who* or *that* as an object pronoun.

LISTENING

📼 Listen to four people talking about things they really hate. Write the number of the speaker by the things they hate.

a People who sit down right next to me on a beach. ☐

b Hotels where the toilets are at the end of the corridor. ☐

c Taxi-drivers who drive over the speed-limit and curse at other drivers. ☐

d Postcards which are impossible to read. ☐

e Smiling airline staff who happily inform you that your plane has been delayed. ☐

f Articles in popular magazines that inform readers of unspoilt beauty spots which tourists haven't found yet. ☐

g Hotel rooms which don't have interesting views. ☐

📼 Listen again and check.

WRITING

Imagine you are the writer of one of the passages in *Reading*. Write a postcard to friends telling them about your experience.

_____

_____

_____

_____

_____

A

We had planned to spend a month on the West Coast of America with some Americans we had met in Scotland. Unfortunately things didn't work out. We didn't know the people we were staying with well and we discovered that we didn't have the same lifestyle as them. They lived in a magnificent house overlooking the sea and employed people who did everything for them. We felt very uncomfortable. Luckily for us, after the first week there was an earthquake which made the house, which was on the top of a cliff, dangerous to live in. So we had to say good-bye to our hosts, who didn't look at all sad to see us go, and we went camping instead. It was certainly the most disappointing holiday I've had for ages.

B

Last spring we rented an old manor house that had been built on the site of an ancient battle ground where thousands of men are supposed to have died. We didn't believe the ghost stories which the housekeeper told us. On the Monday of the second week I was woken up in the night. There were terrible screams and moans coming from the basement. We crept downstairs where the screams were even louder. Terrified, we ran all the way to the village where we spent the rest of the night at a hotel. Next day the housekeeper told us that it was the anniversary of the battle and the screams we had heard were the ghosts of the soldiers who died fighting. We didn't sleep in the house again. It was certainly the most frightening experience I've ever had.

28 | Local produce

VOCABULARY

1 Complete the chart.

Noun	Verb
_____	reduce
building	_____
_____	discover
production	_____
_____	grow
design	_____
_____	increase
invention	_____
_____	distribute

2 Match these manufactured products with the raw materials they are made from. You can use a dictionary.

Manufactured products	Raw materials
bread	petrol
plastic	barley
whisky	iron-ore
cheese	kaolin
steel	wheat
paper	wood
wine	apples
cider	milk
china	grapes

3 Write down products which are manufactured or which come from the following places.

field _tobacco_ _____

distillery _____

vineyard _____

factory _____

power station _____

pottery _____

mine _____

GRAMMAR

1 Write sentences to describe where the products come from.

1 Tobacco/USA _Tobacco is grown in the USA._

2 Whisky/Scotland _____
_____

3 Gold/South Africa _____
_____

4 Beer/Denmark _____
_____

5 Cars/Germany _____
_____

6 Electronic goods/Japan _____
_____

2 Look at the map of France and write sentences using the verbs below.

grow   produce   make   manufacture   mine
design   grow

1 _Melons are grown in the South of France._

2 _____

3 _____

4 _____

5 _____

6 _____

7 _____

3 Complete these sentences using the suitable passive form of the verb in brackets.

1 Coffee _is grown_ in South America. (grow)

2 Today a lot of electronic goods _____ in South-east Asia. (manufacture)

3 It _____ that America _____ by the Vikings. (think, first discover)

4 The ship-building industry _____ over the last ten years. (reduce)

5 No ships _____ there since 1967. (build)

6 Manufactured goods _____ here since the Industrial Revolution. (produce)

7 More raw materials _____ in the future. (import)

8 More milk _____ and _____ all over the country in the next ten years. (process, distribute)

4 Rewrite these sentences in the passive. Start your sentence with the underlined words.

1 They have mined <u>coal</u> in Wales for centuries.
Coal has been mined in Wales for centuries.

2 They export <u>whisky</u> all over the world.
_____
_____

3 Nuclear power is affecting <u>the coal mining industry</u>.
_____
_____

4 They first made <u>pottery</u> here in the 18th century.
_____
_____

5 They were developing <u>the glass industry</u> over 100 years ago.
_____
_____

6 They will increase <u>the production of steel</u>.
_____
_____

WRITING

1 Which words in the list below could you use to describe how and where these manufactured products are made?

cheese _____

paper _____

bread _____

plastic _____

wine _____

ferment milk yeast wheat oven grapes
vineyard trees refined oil chemical process
cook bottle wood pulp water

Write sentences describing how and where the products are made.

_____
_____
_____
_____
_____
_____
_____
_____
_____
_____

2 Use the notes to write about the production of yoghurt.

cows/milked: _____
_____

milk/stored/tank: _____
_____

lorry/collects: _____
_____

take to/dairy: _____
_____

milk/warmed: _____
_____

left to ferment/24 hours: _____
_____

individual pots: _____
_____

deliver/shop: _____
_____

Just what we're looking for!

VOCABULARY

1 Complete the sentences. Choose words from the list.

carpenter electrician builder mechanic
husband plumber gardener decorator

1 I'll get _____ to do the washing up.
2 We'll get _____ to fix the oven.
3 I'll have _____ repaint the hall.
4 He'll get _____ to unblock the toilet.
5 I'll get _____ to plant some fruit trees.
6 We'll have _____ repair the chimney.
7 I'll have _____ make some kitchen cupboards.
8 I'll get _____ to mend the car.

2 Look at the picture and write sentences saying what is wrong with the house.

1 *The shutter is falling off.*
2 _____
3 _____
4 _____
5 _____
6 _____

3 How good are you at working with cars? Look at the chart below and tick (✓) the boxes if you do the things to the car yourself. You can use a dictionary.

	You	Speaker 1	Speaker 2	Speaker 3
clean the car	☐	☐	☐	☐
check the oil	☐	☐	☐	☐
change the oil	☐	☐	☐	☐
check the pressure in the tyres	☐	☐	☐	☐
change the tyres	☐	☐	☐	☐
check the water level in the battery	☐	☐	☐	☐
do minor repairs	☐	☐	☐	☐
mend the brakes	☐	☐	☐	☐
change a fuse	☐	☐	☐	☐

LISTENING

1 🔲 Listen to three people talking about how good they are at working with cars. Complete the chart in *Vocabulary* activity 3 for the three speakers.

2 Who is the most/least self-sufficient?

_____

🔲 Listen again.

GRAMMAR

1 Look at the chart and write six sentences saying what you and the speakers don't do to the car.
1 *I don't mend the brakes myself.*
2 _____
3 _____
4 _____
5 _____
6 _____

2 Write six sentences to say who does the things in 1 to the car. Use the expressions *have it/them done by, get it/them done by.*
1 *I have the brakes mended by a mechanic.*
2 _____
3 _____
4 _____
5 _____
6 _____

3 Write sentences with *need + -ing* for these situations, using the words in brackets.
1 The brakes don't work. (mend, mechanic)
The brakes need mending. I'll get the mechanic to mend them.
2 There is a flat tyre. (change, mechanic)
_____
3 The interior of the car is very dirty. (clean, my father)
_____

4 The battery isn't working properly. (check, a friend)
_____
5 The car won't go. (repair, mechanic)
_____
6 The headlights don't work. (change, someone)
_____

4 Rewrite the sentences above with *need + passive infinitive.*
1 *The brakes need to be mended.*
2 _____
3 _____
4 _____
5 _____
6 _____

WRITING

Write sentences saying what you would do in these situations.
1 The toilet is blocked.
I'd have a plumber fix it immediately.
2 A tree has fallen on your house.
_____
3 The car won't start.
_____
4 You have lost your house keys.
_____
5 You are having a party and you've invited fifty guests.
_____
6 Your car has broken down on a small country road.
_____

30 | *Sporting chance*

VOCABULARY

1 Write down one or two words which you associate with each of these sports.

shooting _____

canoeing _____

skiing _____

car-racing _____

diving _____

climbing _____

white-water rafting _____

swimming _____

tennis _____

basketball _____

football _____

cycling _____

2 Underline the adjectives in the list which you can use with the construction *it is* + adjective + *to* + infinitive. For example: *It's dangerous to drink and drive.*

angry   big   dangerous   easy   essential
expensive   happy   important   necessary   polite
red   right   sensible   sorry   stupid   surprised
tall   unpleasant   wrong

3 Complete the sentences with suitable adjectives from the list.

1 It's _____ to swim after a heavy meal.

2 It's _____ to wear a helmet when you go cycling.

3 It's _____ to wear a life-jacket when you go canoeing.

4 It's _____ to take a guide when you go into the mountains.

5 It's _____ to buy good quality diving equipment.

6 It's _____ to punish people who drink and drive.

7 It's _____ to finish a Football World Cup with penalty shots.

8 It's _____ to shake hands with your opponent after a tennis match.

SOUNDS

Circle the word which has a different vowel sound.

1 sp**or**t   g**oa**l   b**a**ll   sc**or**e   c**our**t

2 r**u**les   p**oo**l   f**oo**t   impr**o**ve   m**o**ve

3 r**a**ce   f**a**st   pl**a**y   l**a**ne   g**a**me

4 dr**u**gs   t**ou**ch   bl**oo**d   m**o**ney   w**oo**den

[cassette] Listen and repeat the words.

GRAMMAR

1 Complete the sentences with *make, let* or *don't let.*

1 They _____ you wear a hard hat when you go horse riding.

2 They _____ you go diving on your own.

3 They _____ athletes have a blood test in the big competitions.

4 They _____ beginners dive in the sea immediately.

5 They _____ players have a drink between games.

6 They _____ spectators sit on the football field.

2 Rewrite the sentences using *make, let* or *don't let.*

1 You have to wear special shoes on a tennis court.
   They make you wear special shoes on a tennis court.

2 You can't go hang gliding until you are sixteen.

   _____

   _____

3 You have to show a medical certificate to take diving lessons.

   _____

   _____

4 Children can't go climbing without an adult.

_____

_____

5 Skiers can't practise on the track before a race.

_____

_____

6 You have to have a licence to own a gun.

_____

_____

7 Children can go on the golf course if they don't make a noise.

_____

_____

READING AND WRITING

1 Look quickly at the newspaper articles 1 to 3 and match them with the titles below. Put the correct letters in the boxes. There is one extra title.

1 ☐   2 ☐   3 ☐

A **NO WINNER IN CHARITY RACE**

B AFRICAN RALLY MAY BE BANNED

C MAN MISTAKES BROTHER FOR RABBIT

D **AMATEUR SKI RACING INCREASINGLY POPULAR**

2 Read the articles and write down the possible causes of the incidents.

1 _____

2 _____

3 _____

3 Write suggestions for improving safety in the sports mentioned in the articles. Use *make* and *let*.

1 *I wouldn't let the rally cars go fast through villages.*

2 _____

3 _____

---

1 A number of competitors in the controversial Trans-Saharan Rally were accused of driving too fast through a village on a busy market day. 'Nobody was hurt, but people were very frightened,' commented a journalist. In the last week a large number of complaints about safety have refuelled the controversy surrounding the rally. The organisers are criticised for not ensuring the safety of spectators and, in particular, for routing the rally through small villages. 'Up until now they have been extremely lucky because there have been no serious incidents. But if the rally continues to race at great speed through small African villages, a serious accident is inevitable,' commented an ex-champion rally driver. Many people are campaigning to ban the rally altogether.

2 All ten rafts participating in an amateur white-water raft race for charity overturned in France yesterday. The race was held on one of France's fastest rivers where heavy rain for over a week had turned the river into a raging torrent and made it extremely difficult to control the rafts. Most of the participants were teenagers and many were not wearing life-jackets or helmets. 'We are extremely lucky that nobody was hurt,' commented one of the organisers. The incident highlights the dangers of this increasingly popular holiday sport. When asked if the charity would organise a similar race next year, the organisers said they had decided to replace white-water rafting by a team ping-pong competition.

3 A man shot his brother in the foot in yet another shooting incident late yesterday evening. The man explained that he had seen something move behind a bush and he had thought it was a rabbit. He fired twice before realising he had made a mistake. The man was shooting rabbits only 50 metres from his home. It was getting dark at the time of the accident. The two brothers were reunited later this morning. They said that they would be having rabbit pie and champagne for supper to celebrate. Where did they get the rabbit? 'From the supermarket! It's far safer and just as tasty,' commented the brothers.

GRAMMAR

1 Complete these sentences with something which is generally true for you.

1 If I have time in the evenings, *I like to go out with my friends.*

2 If the weather is hot at the weekend, _____

_____

3 If I wake up in the night, _____

_____

4 If I have a long train or plane journey, _____

_____

5 If friends come to dinner, _____

_____

2 Rewrite these sentences using *in case*.

1 There is a chance that I'll have to wait, so I usually take my Walkman.
I usually take my Walkman in case I have to wait.

2 There's a chance that it'll rain, so I always take an umbrella.

_____

3 I don't always get time for lunch, so I have a big breakfast.

_____

4 There's always the risk of running out of petrol, so I always take a petrol-can.

_____

5 It's always possible that I'll forget an important appointment, so I always check my agenda.

_____

3 Complete the sentences with *in case* or *if*.

1 We'll take some chocolate _____ we get hungry.

2 I do the shopping on Monday evenings _____ I finish work early.

3 Take a spare key _____ your brother forgets his.

4 Can you drive me to work _____ the bus is late?

5 She usually arrives late _____ the roads are busy.

6 I usually stop off for a coffee _____ I have time.

VOCABULARY

1 Complete the crossword. Write the missing clues using *in case* or *if*.

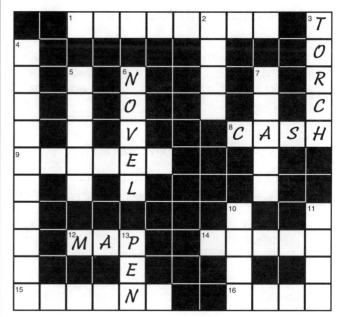

Across

1 In Britain it's always a good idea to carry one in case it rains.

8 _____
_____

9 I stop the car and have one if I am tired.

12 _____

14 Always take one of these in case there isn't one in your hotel room.

15 It's always useful to have a piece in case you need to mend something.

16 I always take an electric one if I go abroad.

Down

2 If you read in bed this can be very useful.

3 _____
_____

4 These can be very useful if you go bird-watching.

5 Always keep one in your bag in case you want to cut something.

6 _____

7 If I have time, I always write down in this what I have done during the day.

10 It is always useful to have this in your bag in case you need a quick wash.

11 Every country has a different one.

13 _____
_____

2 Write down six things you would take with you in each of these situations. List them in order of importance.

1 a trip across the desert _____

_____

2 a holiday on a yacht _____

_____

3 an English exam _____

_____

LISTENING

1 You are going to hear two people talking about the precautions they take before going on holiday. Look at the precautions they take and try to guess the reasons for them. Complete the sentences with *in case*.

1 He/She leaves the holiday address with neighbours *in case they need to contact him.*

2 He/She doesn't leave anything valuable in the house

_____

3 He/She gives a spare house key to a neighbour

_____

4 He/She takes traveller's cheques

_____

5 He/She always takes foreign currency

_____

6 He/She spends the night at the airport

_____

7 He/She leaves for the airport with an hour to spare

_____

8 He/She always takes a good book

_____

9 He/She always takes insect repellent cream

_____

10 He/She takes two packets of aspirin tablets

_____

2 🔊 Listen to the conversation and find out which precautions the man takes and which precautions the woman takes. Circle *He* or *She* as appropriate.

3 Match the reasons below with the precautions 1 to 10 in 1. Put the correct number in the boxes.

a he gets headaches ☐

b the traffic is bad ☐

c there is a power cut ☐

d the exchange bureaux are shut ☐

e they need to contact him ☐

f his bag is stolen ☐

g there is a long wait ☐

h there are insects ☐

i there are burglars ☐

j he misses his plane ☐

🔊 Listen again and check.

WRITING

1 Write sentences about what you do if you have time before work or school, at lunch time, in the evening, at the weekend.

I usually read the newspaper if I have time before I leave for work.

_____

_____

_____

_____

_____

_____

_____

2 Write sentences about the precautions you take when you sit an exam.

I take an aspirin in case I get a headache.

_____

_____

_____

_____

_____

_____

_____

VOCABULARY

What was wrong with the Ford Edsel car?
Match the defects 1 to 9 with the parts of the
car a to i.

Ford produced what must have been the most
defective car of all time in 1957 – the Edsel.
Half of the models sold had any or all of the
following features:

1	windscreen wipers that ❏	a	peeled
2	bonnets and boots that ❏	b	seized up
3	batteries that ❏	c	wouldn't open
4	seatbelts that ❏	d	went flat
5	exhaust pipes that ❏	e	didn't work
6	paint that ❏	f	stopped
7	brakes that ❏	g	failed
8	engines that ❏	h	dropped off
9	speedometers that ❏	i	jammed

LISTENING

1 Look at these sentences and try to guess what
the people who said them are complaining
about.

a 'When I switched it on the first time the picture
was fine but there was no sound.'

_____

b 'Excuse me, but this is rare and I asked for it to
be well done.'

_____

c 'When they were carrying it upstairs they
caused quite a lot of damage.'

_____

d 'We queued up for an hour and were finally
told that the flight had been cancelled.'

_____

e 'When I took it out of the box I found that the
volume button didn't work and the aerial was
broken.'

_____

f 'It is impossible to assemble the drawers
because there are several bits missing from the
box.'

_____

g 'It's still leaking all over the floor when it's on
rinse.'

_____

2 🔲 Now listen to four people making
complaints. Match the sentences in 1 with the
conversations. Did you guess correctly? If not,
what things are the complaints about? Choose
from the list below.

kitchen cupboard kit   washing machine
radio   undercooked steak   cancelled flight
television   wardrobe

Conversation 1 _____

Conversation 2 _____

Conversation 3 _____

Conversation 4 _____

Do the people complaining obtain satisfaction
or not?

3 Put the verbs in either the present simple,
present perfect or the future.

1 I _____ (send) the technician round to
have a look at it as soon as he _____
(finish) with a customer.

2 I _____ (explain) the problem to the
manager when he _____ (come in).

3 I _____ (be) pleased to help you when
you _____ (find) the receipt.

4 I _____ (send) the delivery van round
as soon as it _____ (get in).

🔲 Listen to the conversations again and
check your answers.

GRAMMAR

1 Underline the correct verb form.

1 *He come/He'll come* round after I *finish/have finished* in the office.

2 When the parts arrive, *we send/we'll send* a mechanic.

3 *I'll phone/I phone* as soon as I can.

4 I'll contact you after I *have seen/will see* my lawyer.

5 As soon as I receive your letter, *I'll make/I make* suitable arrangements.

6 When *you bring/you will bring* it to the garage, *we check/we'll check* the brakes.

[cassette] Listen and check.

2 [cassette] Listen and complete these sentences with *due to, expected to,* or *likely to.*

1 When do you think he's _____ come?

2 It is more _____ be in the afternoon.

3 He is _____ arrive at about three thirty.

4 We are _____ receive spare parts for that particular make sometime next week.

5 When are you _____ be able to bring it round?

6 The mechanic is _____ arrive at four.

[cassette] Listen again and check.

READING AND WRITING

1 The sentences below come from a letter of complaint but are in the wrong order. Put them in the right order and number them 1 to 10.

a They then smashed a mirror and two vases as they were carrying the wardrobe upstairs. ☐

b Naturally, I expect a complete refund and compensation for the damage caused by your delivery men. ☐

c I am writing to you about the antique wardrobe I bought from your furniture showroom in the High Street on 18th September. ☐

d When they finally got it into the bedroom I noticed that the wood on one side was badly scratched. ☐

e Dear Sir or Madam, ☐

f I would be grateful if you would send someone competent round to collect the wardrobe as soon as possible. ☐

g I look forward to hearing from you. Yours faithfully, ☐

h I insisted that they took the wardrobe back to the shop because of the condition it was in but they refused and told me to get in touch with you. ☐

i As arranged, it was brought to my house by your delivery service on the day following the purchase. ☐

j As the men were carrying it into the house they broke a panel of the front door. ☐

2 Write a letter of reply to the letter in 1. Include the following points.

– your address   – the date   – greetings

– acknowledgement of letter of complaint

– inform the buyer that you are not responsible for delivery service because it is a separate company

– advise them to send complaints directly to their office

– give the address of the delivery company (Removals Express Service, 29, Black St, Bash-on-Weir. Tel: 01932 543 876)

– apologise and hope they manage to get full satisfaction

– inform them that you have some interesting pieces of furniture in the showroom

– closing remarks   – signature and name

_____

_____

_____

_____

_____

_____

_____

_____

_____

GRAMMAR

1 Underline the clause of purpose in each of these sentences. Then rewrite each sentence by putting the clause of purpose at the end of the sentence.

1 <u>To keep lettuce crisp</u>, store it in a plastic bag.
Store lettuce in a plastic bag to keep it crisp.

2 To stay awake on a long journey, drink coffee.

_____

3 To remove stains from dirty silver, leave it to soak in Coca Cola.

_____

4 To make your windows really shine, clean them with wet newspaper.

_____

5 To get rid of the smell of cigarette smoke, leave a candle burning.

_____

6 To stop peeled potatoes going black, pour a little vinegar in the water.

_____

2 Match the two parts of the sentences to give advice. Put the correct numbers in the boxes.

1 If you spill oil on your trousers,
2 If you pour wine on the carpet,
3 If you have hiccups,
4 If you want shiny teeth,
5 If your windscreen is very dirty,

☐ a put salt on it immediately.

☐ b brush them occasionally with salt.

☐ c rub it with an onion to make it shine.

☐ d rub butter on the stain before washing them.

☐ e ask a friend to frighten you.

SOUNDS

🔊 Listen and repeat these sentences. Notice the stress and intonation in sentences with two parts.

1 To make your table shine, rub it with warm vinegar.
2 If you spill red wine on the carpet, pour salt on it immediately.
3 If you get a stain on your T-shirt, wear it back-to-front.
4 To make silver shine, soak it in Coca Cola.
5 To stop potatoes going brown, add lemon juice to the water.
6 If you burn your hand, hold it in cold water for five minutes.

VOCABULARY

1 Label the objects in the pictures with the words below. Use *a, an* or *some*.

ice-cube   lettuce   windscreen   toothpaste
fly   tie   hairdryer   tomatoes   ashtray   matches
fridge   shoes

2 How good is your memory? Look at the objects for exactly one minute. Then close the book and write down as many of the objects as you can remember.

Did you remember all the objects in activity 1? How did you try to memorise the objects?

3 For each object, write down one adjective and one verb which you associate with it.

1 *ice cube: cold, freeze*   7 _____
2 _____   8 _____
3 _____   9 _____
4 _____   10 _____
5 _____   11 _____
6 _____   12 _____

READING

1 Read the extract from the guide *How to improve your memory* and match each paragraph in the passage with a heading below.

Substitution   Rhymes   Classification   Association

2 Read the passage again and underline all the clauses of purpose.

3 Complete the statements with information from the passage.

1 _____ , you can improve your memory.

2 To remember new information, _____
_____

3 To remember names, _____
_____

4 If you want to remember something abstract,
_____

5 You can remember lists of words or objects by
_____

6 You can train yourself to associate things by
_____

4 Do you think any of the techniques mentioned in the passage are likely to be useful to you for learning English?

How to improve your memory

For most of us there is no such thing as a 'poor' memory – just a trained or an untrained one. You can nearly always improve your memory by training yourself in a number of simple techniques.

a) _____
All memory is based on association. You can remember any new piece of information by associating it with something you already know. For example:
– to spell the word 'piece', think of a piece of pie.
– to recall the shape of Italy, think of a boot.
You can train yourself to associate things by asking the questions why, when, how, where and who. Answering these questions will help you form a complete picture of the item and enable you to remember it.

b) _____
You can use substitution to remember abstract information when it is not easy to imagine a picture of what is being learned. When you hear or see a word that seems abstract or intangible, think of anything that sounds like or reminds you of the word you want to remember. For instance, if you want to remember a name, associate it with a visual image.
Mike – Microphone, Bill – Electricity bill

c) _____
It is certainly not easy to recall a list of objects arbitrarily grouped together. Whenever you deal with several items, you can remember them more easily by dividing them into groups. It is possible to classify things in many different categories. Each person will have their own way of grouping things together.

d) _____
Children often learn short rhymes to help them remember things that are very often a problem. Many people still use these memory aids even when they are adults.
For instance, to spell the words 'receive' and 'believe' and to remember which takes 'ie' and which takes 'ei', children learn this rhyme:
I before E except after C.

SOUNDS

1 Underline the stressed syllables in these pairs of words. Tick (✓) the pairs where the stress shifts.

1 e<u>co</u>nomy   eco<u>no</u>mic
2 appreciate   appreciation
3 consume   consumption
4 energy   energetic
5 environment   environmental
6 hospitable   hospitality
7 accommodate   accommodation

🔊 Listen and check. Say the words aloud.

2 Look at these words. Which ones contain the sounds /g/ or /dʒ/? Which words contain a silent 'g'? Put them in three columns.

damage   energy   foreign   give   guide   guest
language   sights   suggestion

/g/	/dʒ/	silent 'g'
_____	_____	_____
_____	_____	_____
_____	_____	_____
_____	_____	_____

🔊 Listen and say the words aloud.

READING

1 Read the passage and write a suitable title for it.

_____

2 There are five sentences which do not belong in the passage. Find and underline them.

Adventure travel is travel you can experience with all your senses. The adventure traveller is an individual who will use independent modes of transport that enable him/her to go where and when he/she pleases. The adventure traveller often enjoys travelling alone. If you travel alone, you will need to be very independent and self-sufficient. If you reduce your petrol consumption, you will save money. You'll need to think about everything very carefully, especially if you go to remote areas. If you travel with another person, make sure you choose your companion carefully. In remote but inhabited places you will probably be the focus of interest, so make sure you are always patient, respectful and friendly. Avoid buying plastic bottles, they pollute the oceans. Locals will appreciate this and will be friendly and hospitable in return. If you take people's addresses, do write to them, it will mean a lot.

If you are walking, you will require the minimum of equipment. If everyone uses less electricity, there will be less nuclear waste. But as soon as you leave the roads and head for the mountains you will need equipment that is a lot more specialised. Climbing with a guide will lead you into a new exciting world which on your own you would probably miss. If you are cycling, you can put your things in panniers so you won't have a heavy pack on your back. If you take a shower instead of a bath, you will save water. You can cover greater distances than on foot, but at a pace that allows real appreciation and discovery.

Travelling with horses, camels or yaks is exciting but you need some experience. If you buy a microwave oven, you will use less energy. They don't go as fast as you might think. And camels do need to drink!

Adventure travel is primarily a question of independence, determination and confidence. Anyone with an adventurous spirit can do it. The sense of achievement and self-confidence that come from it are immeasurable. Don't hesitate, pack this guide in your rucksack and go – you will never look back!

3 The five extra sentences are all about the same topic. Tick (✓) the correct topic.

1 public transport ☐   2 conservation ☐

3 electricity ☐   4 waste recycling ☐

4 Complete the sentences with information from the passage.

1 If you are adventurous, you *will enjoy travelling alone.*

2 If you travel alone, _____

3 If you go to remote areas, _____

4 If you travel with another person, _____

5 If you go to remote but inhabited areas, _____

6 If you are respectful and friendly, _____

7 If you take people's addresses, _____

8 If you go into the mountains, _____

9 If you go with a guide, _____

10 If you have a bicycle with panniers, _____

5 What sort of traveller are you? Does adventure travel appeal to you?

_____
_____
_____
_____

GRAMMAR

1 Put the words in order and write sentences. Remember to separate the clauses with a comma (,).

1 Greece you if to have you weather good go will

_____
_____

2 travel if of avoid you season will crowds out you

_____
_____

3 if don't will a take guide get book lost you you

_____
_____

4 don't won't heat like like the you you Morocco if

_____
_____

5 will you India spicy you if appreciate enjoy food

_____
_____

2 Complete these sentences with the present simple or the future tense of the verbs.

1 If you ___*like*___ (like) the seaside, you ___*will enjoy*___ (enjoy) Florida.

2 You _____ (discover) some beautiful sights if you _____ (hire) a guide.

3 If you _____ (stay) in a hotel, the holiday _____ (cost) a lot of money.

4 You _____ (spend) so much if you _____ (travel) by coach.

5 If you _____ (have) enough money, you _____ (enjoy) your stay.

6 If you _____ (like) snow, you _____ (enjoy) Norway in winter.

WRITING

Write a few sentences about what will happen to our environment in the future if we don't take action now. Think about these things:

the ozone layer   the greenhouse effect   acid rain
the oceans   wildlife

_____
_____
_____
_____
_____
_____

Lost in the Pacific

READING

1 Read the short story *Reflection* and find out who Frank Todd is and why he decides to change his job.

Reflection

Frank should have looked before stepping off the pavement. His face wore a mask of terror. The last thing Frank Todd saw before he died was a huge truck hurtling towards him.

Frank shot up from his pillow, frightened. He had woken his wife, June, by his sudden movement, and she switched on the bedside lamp. 'Frank, it's all right,' she said. She had seen Frank like this many times before. He had been having the dream regularly for the past year now.

'I saw it coming, June. It was coming straight at me. I ... I couldn't get out of the way,' he stammered.

It was ironic that Frank should dream of being knocked down by a truck. He was himself a truck driver, and had been one for twenty-one years. He owned his own truck now and things had been going well for him until ten months earlier, when the dreams started. They were always the same: a large truck would appear, hurtling towards him. It all seemed so real.

She felt sure that the dreams would stop if he did. Frank had resisted at first, but the more he thought about it, the more he thought June might be right. And this morning he had a surprise for her. 'I start in a week's time, after I finish my last delivery,' he said. June was delighted.

Frank was on one of his regular journeys. But this was to be his last. He hoped that by getting away from trucks completely the dreams would stop. Frank thought about his new job and he momentarily lost his concentration and failed to notice the pedestrian about to step into the road. Instinctively, Frank hit the brakes. The pedestrian turned to see the huge truck hurtling towards him. Frank saw his face. It wore a mask of terror.

A thought flashed through Frank's head. 'It's happening. The dream is coming true. But it's not me, it's not ...' The truck was out of control and heading straight for ...

'Oh no!' Frank screamed.

The last thing Frank Todd saw before he died was the glass-fronted tower he crashed into, shattering into a thousand pieces the vivid reflection that had been terrifying him for so long: the reflection of a huge truck hurtling towards him.

2 How did Frank's dream predict the future? Put a tick (✓) by the correct sentence.

1 Frank Todd was run over by a truck. ☐

2 Frank Todd ran a pedestrian over with his truck. ☐

3 Frank Todd crashed his truck into a glass-fronted building. ☐

3 Read the story again and decide where these sentences go. The sentences are in the order in which they appear in the story.

1 He had had a dream, a terrible dream.

2 He had started with a five-tonner and then he moved on to big ones.

3 June had asked Frank many times recently to quit trucking and take another job.

4 He told her that he had taken a job with the council as a gardener.

5 It was one he had done many times before.

GRAMMAR

1 Look at these sentences from the passage. What are the verb tenses?

1 He had been having the dream regularly for the past year.

2 She had seen Frank like this many times before.

2 Complete the sentences with *when, after* or *because*. Underline the action which happened first.

1 She had been a truck driver for twenty-one years _____ she finally got another job.

2 She decided to retire _____ she had flown around the world.

3 She went to live in the country _____ she had made her last delivery.

4 _____ she had broken the record, she gave up flying.

5 She went to live in California _____ her husband worked there.

6 She didn't want to see her parents _____ she had been unhappy as a child.

7 Jack wanted to change his job _____ truck driving had exhausted him.

3 Change these sentences into reported speech. Remember to use the past perfect.

1 'I always wanted to be a truck driver,' he said.
He said he had always wanted to be a
truck driver.

2 'He tried to stop the truck in time,' she said.
_____
_____

3 'I enjoyed my job before the dreams started,' he said.
_____
_____

4 'I didn't see the documentary about Amelia Earhart,' she said.
_____
_____

5 'She worked hard until she retired,' he said.
_____
_____

4 Underline the actions which happened first in these sentences from the passage:

1 Things had been going well for him until ten months earlier when the dreams started.

2 The last thing Frank Todd saw was the vivid reflection that had been terrifying him for so long.

5 Join these sentences with *when* or *until*, using the past perfect continuous.

1 He enjoyed his job. The dreams started.
He had been enjoying his job until the
dreams started.

2 He tried to avoid the pedestrian. The truck hit the glass tower.
_____
_____

3 She flew over the Pacific Ocean. The plane crashed.
_____
_____

4 He had the same dream for a year. He died.
_____
_____

5 He lived comfortably for several years. He lost his job.
_____
_____

6 She flew for twenty years. She disappeared.
_____
_____

VOCABULARY

1 Look at the list of words. Underline those which were used in the passage about Amelia Earhart. Circle those which were used in the short story about the truck driver.

brakes capture concentration control crash
delivery destroyed died disappear dream
drown equator exhausted feminism fuel
gardener glass huge hurtling mask mystery
pavement pedestrian pieces pillow
propaganda record reflection retire rumour
screamed solo strained survive terror
tower true

2 Choose six words from the list above and write sentences.

1 _____
2 _____
3 _____
4 _____
5 _____
6 _____

3 Write a few sentences about a man or woman from your country who achieved something remarkable. Use the past perfect if possible.
_____
_____
_____
_____
_____
_____

36 | *What's your advice?*

SOUNDS

🔊 Listen to these sentences. Put a tick (✓) if the speaker sounds friendly and a cross (✗) if the advice sounds like a warning.

1 You ought to spend more time with your family. ☐

2 You really ought to get here on time. ☐

3 If I were you, I'd only have a light meal before the exam. ☐

4 You really should visit the Louvre. ☐

5 You shouldn't let it spoil the relationship. ☐

6 If I were you, I'd be careful of what you say. ☐

🔊 Listen again and check. Say the sentences aloud.

GRAMMAR

1 Complete the sentences with the past simple or *would* + infinitive. Use the verbs from the list below.

find out   go out   know   marry
settle down   tell

1 If I _____ him, he'd be very upset.

2 She wouldn't get involved if she _____ he was married.

3 If I were you, I _____ yet.

4 It would spoil their relationship if she _____ about the affair.

5 If they _____ together, it wouldn't last long.

6 If she _____ him, her parents would be very upset.

2 Write advice for these situations. Use *if I were you*, *should* or *ought to*.

1 I'm sitting an English exam tomorrow.
I think you ought to go to bed early.
_____

2 I'm having a week's holiday in New York.
_____
_____

3 My car won't start this morning.
_____
_____

4 My credit card has disappeared.
_____
_____

5 I've spilled ketchup down my suit.
_____
_____

6 I'm taking my new girlfriend out.
_____
_____

3 In what circumstances would you do the following things?

1 call the police
I'd call the police if I saw a burglar
breaking into a house.

2 live in a foreign country
_____
_____

3 buy a bottle of champagne
_____
_____

4 go to the dentist's
_____
_____

5 learn Chinese
_____
_____

6 buy a mobile phone
_____
_____

READING

1 **Read the situations below and write what you would do.**

1   As you run along the platform to catch your train which is just leaving, you knock over an old lady's bag and all her belongings fall out. *I'd shout an apology and jump on the train.*

2   Your partner snores very loudly and keeps you awake. The trouble is he/she won't believe you when you tell him/her.

3   You go to the hairdresser's for a wash and cut and you come out with an orange frizzy mess.

4   A friend repays a £10 debt and you realise the next day that the bank note is a fake.

5   Your neighbour phones to inform you that her pedigree collie bitch has just given birth to ten puppies and that your dog is the father. She wants to know what you intend to do.

6   You are going on a short but important business trip to Japan and you are worried about how you will cope with the difficult negotiations if you are suffering from the effects of jet lag.

7   A good friend is staying with you because his marriage is breaking up and he needs a place to stay. He spends a lot of time on the phone when you are out and has run up a big bill. Unfortunately he hasn't offered to pay for the calls and you know he has financial problems.

8   You accidentally damage a parked car. You don't know who it belongs to and there is nobody in sight.

2 **Match the advice below with the situations 1 to 8 in activity 1. Put the correct numbers in the boxes.**

a   If I were you, I'd take it straight to the police.   ☐

b   You should show him the bill and ask for a contribution.   ☐

c   If I were you, I'd shout an apology and jump on the train.   ☐

d   You should offer to pay the vet's bill to have the animals put down.   ☐

e   If I were you, I'd kick him/her.   ☐

f   If I were you, I'd drive away as quickly as possible.   ☐

g   You should refuse to pay and ask to see the person in charge.   ☐

h   You should take a sleeping tablet and sleep for the whole flight.   ☐

LISTENING

1   🔊 **Listen to three conversations. Match the conversations with the situations in *Reading* activity 1. Put the numbers of the situations in the correct boxes.**

Conversation 1   ☐
Conversation 2   ☐
Conversation 3   ☐

2 **What advice do the people give for each situation?**

1   _____

2   _____

3   _____

🔊 Listen again and check.

GRAMMAR

1 Rewrite the sentences using *ought to have* or *oughtn't to have*.

1 He should've gone to Hong Kong in the autumn.

He ought to have gone to Hong Kong in the autumn.

2 She shouldn't have worn flip-flops in the restaurant.

_____

_____

3 He shouldn't have eaten so much dinner.

_____

_____

4 You should've told me where you were going.

_____

_____

5 They should've checked the price of the room first.

_____

_____

6 We shouldn't have bought so many cigarettes.

_____

_____

2 What did these people do wrong? Write sentences saying what they should and shouldn't have done.

1 When my Korean host invited me to the restaurant, I insisted on paying the bill. I wanted to show him grateful I was for his hospitality. Unfortunately, it seemed to make him very upset. **– Jasper**

He should have let his host pay the bill.

_____

2 The man who told me to leave the mosque looked quite angry. He said something about it being forbidden to film people at prayer, and he kept pointing at my shoes. **– Molly**

_____

3 I got some very strange looks from passers-by when I ate my hamburger in the street. And one day when I blew my nose in class, all my Japanese students giggled. **– Helena**

_____

_____

SOUNDS

1 🔲 Listen and repeat the sentences in *Grammar* activity 1.

2 Circle the word with a different vowel sound.

1 good   food   pool   group
2 junk   humid   summer stuff
3 scarce shared fair   wait
4 peak   cheap   wear   piece

🔲 Listen and check.

VOCABULARY

Look at the pictures on the next page and write down words you could use to talk about holidays in these places. Where do you think they are? Can you say what time of year it is?

Picture A _____

Picture B _____

Picture C _____

LISTENING

1 🔲 Listen and match the conversations with the pictures. Put the correct letters in the boxes.

Conversation 1 ☐ _____
Conversation 2 ☐ _____
Conversation 3 ☐ _____

Did the people enjoy their holidays in these places? Write *yes* or *no*.

2 🔊 Listen to Conversation 1 again and write down five words the speakers use to describe the place and the people.

_____

_____

3 🔊 Listen to Conversation 2 again and underline the words you wrote down in *Vocabulary* which the speakers use.

_____

_____

4 Write down four things that the woman in Conversation 2 should have done.

She should have visited Budapest in the spring.

_____

_____

5 🔊 Listen to Conversation 3 again and write down four things the woman ought to have done and four things she should not have done.

She ought to have taken the train to the airport.

_____

_____

_____

She shouldn't have gone to the airport by car.

_____

_____

_____

_____

WRITING

1 Look at the sentences in *Grammar* activity 1. Write a sentence describing what the person probably did or did not do.

1 *He probably went to Hong Kong in the spring when it was wet.*

2 _____

_____

3 _____

_____

4 _____

_____

5 _____

6 _____

2 Write about a place you have visited for a holiday or for work. Say what you did, where you stayed and the places you visited. Write about things that you didn't do or see and that you regret not doing or seeing. Use as many words from your list in *Vocabulary* as you can.

_____

_____

_____

_____

_____

_____

_____

GRAMMAR

Do these pairs of sentences mean the same? Put a tick (✓) if they are the same or a cross (✗) if they are different.

1 He must have finished work by now.
   He should have finished work by now. ☐

2 They might have forgotten his birthday.
   They may have forgotten his birthday. ☐

3 They could have taken the car.
   They must have taken the car. ☐

4 She can't have disappeared.
   She may have disappeared. ☐

5 I could have left it at the post office.
   I may have left it at the post office. ☐

READING

1 Read the first paragraph of the story *The corridor* and find out where the person is and why he is there.

The **corridor**

His heart-beat had slowed down to normal now. If that had been a trick it hadn't worked. He didn't believe any of their stories about this place anyway. Haunted houses – he had left all that nonsense behind him with his childhood! And he could never resist a bet, however small. As well they knew.

Now read the rest of the story and check your answers.

The corridor was uncarpeted, so that his footsteps clicked loudly as he walked. The only light came through the open doors of the empty rooms down each side, and this light was fading fast. At the far end was a wall on which somebody had hung a full-length mirror. When he had first seen the figure walking towards him it had given him a nasty shock, until he realised it was his own reflection.

Finding that he was sweating slightly, he reached into his right-hand pocket, pulled out his handkerchief and wiped his forehead. He lifted <u>his left hand</u> and glanced at his watch. The idea had been for him to spend half an hour in here after sunset, alone. There was no reason why he should walk any further along the corridor, but it would pass the time. So he walked on, <u>feeling an absurd impulse to salute his image as it approached</u>. They were within touching distance now. Their eyes met.

Suddenly the reflection, the mirror and the wall vanished. Instead, there was another corridor, stretching ahead of him into darkness. <u>He stopped, but the footsteps carried on, clicking away behind him and fading into silence. He turned to find he was facing a blank wall</u>.

Sweating again, <u>he reached into his left pocket, pulled out his handkerchief</u>, and mopped his brow. <u>He glanced at the watch on his right wrist ...</u>

It was dark now. The two young men waited uneasily on the gravel path in front of the building.

'Here he comes!' said one with relief. 'Well? See anything? No? Never mind, you've won your bet. Come on, we'll get that pint!'

'I bet you're glad to be out of there, all the same,' said the other friend as the three walked away.

<u>The figure in the middle smiled and nodded its head vigorously.</u>

2 Put these sentences in the correct order and number them 1 to 6.

☐ a He walked up to the mirror.

☐ b He walked down the empty corridor as it was going dark.

☐ c The mirror suddenly disappeared.

☐ d He saw himself in a mirror at the end of the corridor.

☐ e He heard footsteps.

☐ f He was facing a blank wall.

3 Answer the questions and try to guess the meanings of the words or phrases.

1 *fading*: Was it getting darker or lighter?

2 *sweating*: Why did he wipe his forehead with a handkerchief?

3 *impulse*: Is this a sudden idea or a careful decision?

4 *vanished*: Was the mirror still there or had it disappeared?

5 *mopped his brow*: What did he do with the handkerchief?

4 Look again at the parts of the story which are underlined. Can you say why they are strange?

_____

_____

_____

_____

5 What do you think happened to the man as he was walking down the corridor? Who do you think came out of the house?

Write as many possible explanations as you can using past modals.

_____

_____

_____

_____

_____

SOUNDS

Match the words with the same vowel sounds.

1	heart	a	come
2	mopped	b	beat
3	turn	c	glance
4	find	d	gone
5	wrist	e	through
6	reach	f	learn
7	clue	g	tiles
8	won	h	miss

🔈 Listen and check.

VOCABULARY

Match the definitions below with words from the lists in *Sounds*.

1 An important part of our body.

_____

2 What the part of our body in 1 does all our life.

_____

3 Between the arm and the hand.

_____

4 Look at something quickly.

_____

39 | *Making the grade*

GRAMMAR

1 Write explanations of the meaning of these sentences.

1 I wish I could play the piano.
   I can't play the piano.

2 I wish we had won the match.
   _____

3 I wish I had studied economics instead of computer programming.
   _____

4 If only I hadn't left him alone that day.
   _____

5 If only your mother would let you come to the festival.
   _____

6 I wish we didn't have to leave before the end.
   _____

7 If only I had worked harder at school.
   _____

8 I wish you had warned me before I left.
   _____

2 Write wishes for the future or regrets about the past.

1 It's a pity I can't speak Russian.
   I wish I spoke Russian.

2 I was really stupid not to go to university.
   _____

3 Unfortunately, I never knew my grandparents.
   _____

4 I'm a dreadful cook. Sometimes it's a real nuisance.
   _____

5 Unfortunately, I've lost touch with my cousins.
   _____

6 I have a really boring job.
   _____

3 Rewrite the sentences in activity 2 using *if only*.

1 *If only I spoke Russian.*
2 _____
3 _____
4 _____
5 _____
6 _____

LISTENING

1 🔲 Listen to three people talking about their schooldays. What types of school did they go to? Did they like or dislike school?

Speaker 1 _____

Speaker 2 _____

Speaker 3 _____

2 🔲 Listen again and write the number of the speaker by the things they regret.

a not speaking Spanish today ☐

b giving up languages ☐

c spending a lot of time doing homework ☐

d choosing Latin ☐

e being unhappy at school ☐

f not enjoying myself more ☐

g not working harder at school ☐

h failing my exams ☐

i not going to a boarding school ☐

j not doing Spanish ☐

3 Write sentences expressing regrets for the things a to f in activity 2.

1 *I wish I could speak Spanish.*

2 _____

3 _____

4 _____

5 _____

6 _____

READING

1 In the poem *Aphasia* below, the poet speaks for a child who suffers from the condition of aphasia. Children suffering from aphasia have great difficulty understanding speech and learning to speak themselves. Are these children likely to have a happy or an unhappy relationship with words? Read the poem and find out.

Aphasia

I'm seven, and I'm dead bright,
But words give me a fright.
Words are bullies.
Sneaky things. They gabble and lie.
Sometimes trying to understand
Them makes me cry. Words hurt.
Words are all over the place.
They get shoved in my face.
I don't know why but
Words make me cry.

I wish words were things
You could hug,
Or that they smelt nice.
I wish they came in bottles
Like fizzy-drinks, or melted
Like ice-cream. But they don't.
Words are mean. They bully me.
Lock me away
From what I want to say.

I can't even ask for help,
And I'm only seven
(And a bit).
Words spread nasty gossip.
They must. Otherwise why
Would people think I'm thick?

Words
They make me sick
Inside.

2 Answer the questions and try to guess the meanings of the words.

1 *bright:* Is this likely to mean intelligent or stupid?

2 *bullies:* Are these sort of people kind or unkind to others?

3 *lie:* If you lie do you tell the truth or not?

4 *hug:* Are you likely to hold something nice close to you or push it away?

5 *mean:* Does the child think words are nice or unpleasant?

6 *lock me away:* Do words isolate the child from other people or help him/her communicate?

7 *thick:* Is this likely to mean intelligent or stupid?

3 Which words or phrases in the poem mean the same as these sentences?

1 The child is seven years old.
   _____

2 The child is intelligent.
   _____

3 The child suffers because he/she can't communicate.
   _____

4 The child can't understand what people say.
   _____

5 The child feels isolated because he/she can't express him/herself.
   _____

6 The child doesn't trust words.
   _____

7 The child thinks that words don't tell the truth.
   _____

4 Which of these statements do you think the poet would agree with? Tick the boxes.

1 Children suffering from aphasia are unhappy because they feel isolated. ☐

2 These children live in their own world and cut themselves off from other people. ☐

3 For these children words are enemies. ☐

5 Underline the phrases in the poem which express wishes. Write sentences expressing what you think the child really wishes.

I wish words didn't make me cry.

_____

_____

_____

6 📼 Listen to the poem.

VOCABULARY

1 The words below are all the same part of speech. Can you say what it is?

beckon   curse   encounter   flicker   follow
frown   gleam   grab   laugh   murder   picnic
threaten   whistle

Underline the words which are also nouns.

2 Complete the sentences with words from the list. Use the correct form of the verbs.

1 The first _____ with the man took place in a café.

2 She couldn't see him but she could hear him _____ a pop tune outside.

3 The bank robber _____ to shoot the cashier if she didn't give him the money.

4 They decided to have a _____ by the river.

5 Whenever he looked round the man was behind him. He was sure the man _____ him.

6 The story of the dreadful _____ was on the front page of all the newspapers.

7 The comedian made them all _____ .

SOUNDS

1 Underline the silent letters.

building   laugh   neighbourhood   whistle   though
frighten   grandmother   night   sign   would

Listen and say the words aloud.

2 Circle the word which has a different vowel sound.

1 building   picnic   convinced   notice   stride

2 frown   fellow   follow   radio   rolling

3 around   encounter   journey   house   now

4 murder   curse   turned   learn   sure

Listen and check.

3 How do you pronounce the vowel group 'ea' in these words? Put the words in four groups: /e/ , /ɜː/, /iː/ and /eɪ/ .

threaten   heard   beat   breath   breathing   break
leave   reading   gleam   dead

/e/	/ɜː/	/iː/	/eɪ/

Listen and say the words aloud.

GRAMMAR

1 Match the two parts of the sentence. Put the letters in the boxes.

☐ 1 If they hadn't passed their exams

☐ 2 If they had stopped selling weapons

☐ 3 If they hadn't run out of cigarettes

☐ 4 If the government had not spent so much

☐ 5 If they had worked harder at school

a they wouldn't have gone out to the shop.

b the economy would not be in such a bad state today.

c they would have been able to go to university.

d they would have gone abroad for a year.

e the war would not have lasted so long.

2 Say what would/wouldn't have happened if things had been different.

1 Fred/sent to prison for stealing/found a job
Fred wouldn't have been sent to prison for stealing if he had found a job.

2 I/walk home/miss the bus

_____

3 Helen/get very wet/forget her umbrella

_____

4   Chloé/very upset/you not come to see her

_____

5   Dieter/join the local football club earlier/hear about it

_____

6   Felix/miss the flight/go to the meeting

_____

READING

1 Look quickly at the newspaper articles and match them to the titles below. Put the letter of the article by the title.

1   Vanity was his downfall ☐

2   Unlucky couple throw winning tickets away ☐

3   Return to sender ☐

4   Sand in their eyes ☐

2 Read the newspaper articles and say what would/would not have happened or what might have happened if things had been different.

_____
_____
_____
_____
_____
_____
_____
_____

3 Answer the questions and try to guess the meaning of the words and expressions.

1   *crook*: Is this the robber or a bank clerk?

2   *obeyed*: Did the woman give him the money?

3   *smuggling*: Is this likely to be something illegal or legal?

4   *forger*: Is this someone who makes false money or someone who paints portraits?

5   *heartbroken*: Were they unhappy or happy?

6   *rubbish tip*: Where do things that have been thrown away go?

A A bank in Reno, Nevada, was the scene of a hold-up which went wrong. The crook walked casually up to the cashier and handed her a note. It instructed her to put all the money into a bag and hand it over. The frightened woman obeyed and the crook escaped into the crowded city streets. But there was a nasty shock for him when he reached home. The police were waiting to arrest him. The note he had given the cashier had been written on the back of an envelope. On the other side was his name and address.

B Twice a week a Belgian riding a bicycle crossed the German border and he always carried a suitcase filled with sand. Each time the customs officials searched the suitcase, they never found anything illegal. Sometimes they even emptied out all the sand, expecting to find jewellery, watches or drugs. But always there was nothing but sand. They couldn't think what the Belgian was smuggling. It was many years later, long after the Belgian had vanished from the scene, that they learned the truth. He had been smuggling bicycles.

C Kenyan police had no difficulty identifying and catching a master forger who produced near-perfect bank notes. Instead of printing a portrait of the president on the notes he used a picture of himself.

D The Peters family were heartbroken when they realised they had won £100,000 in a football draw and they had thrown away the prize-winning tickets. Because they had not read the rules carefully they thought their tickets were of no use. They spent all afternoon searching for the tickets at the local rubbish tip but with no luck. A man from Hammersmith won the prize instead.

Tapescripts

Lesson 1   Listening, activity 2

INT.   When did you come to live in Britain, Dan?
DAN   It's been over five years now. Um, I came here after university to visit my grandparents. I'd never met them because, well, they couldn't afford the journey to Australia. I didn't really intend to settle here, but I got this job for an oil company which needed professional divers. I'd worked as a diving instructor back home so, well, I thought it might be interesting to work for this British oil company for a couple of years. I really enjoy it. It's, er, it's pretty dangerous work, but, well, that just makes it more interesting. I travel all over the world which is, you know, one of the things I like most about the job. I haven't been back home to Australia for, ooh, two years now. But I don't miss it very much. I don't get time to. Just my parents and brother, but I speak to them on the phone every week.

Lesson 1   Listening, activities 3 and 4

INT.   What about your personal life, Dan? Are you married?
DAN   No. I'm single and I don't think that'll change for some time yet! I love travelling and I rarely stay long enough in the same place to get to know people well. I suppose one day I may get fed up with this kind of life, but for the moment, well, I'm just making the most of it.
INT.   What sort of social life do you have with all this travelling?
DAN   When I'm diving, none at all. In my line it's important to be on top form all the time, so late nights are out. When I have a few days off, I go out to a nightclub or a restaurant with the guys I work with.
INT.   What about the future? How long do you think you'll go on diving for a living?
DAN   Um, I really don't know. I live from one day to the next and never worry about the future. But, most divers don't carry on beyond the age of about forty.

Lesson 2   Listening, activity 2

Speaker 1   Well, we're leaving on Saturday. We're going to Vancouver for the first week and then on to the mountains for a few days. We're flying, of course, because it's such a long way. The children are really looking forward to it because it's their first flight. Um, we're staying at a hotel outside town and we're hiring a car so we can see the area. We're coming back on the 29th July and my husband's starting back at work on the following Monday. I'm lucky, I've got another week off to do things with the kids.

Speaker 2
WOMAN   What are the arrangements for tomorrow, John?
MAN   Er, you're taking the seven o'clock train from Grand Central to Boston. Our branch manager's meeting you at the station at 8.30 and driving you to the office. At 9.30 you're attending a meeting with the other directors. You're having lunch together at the International Hotel at 1 o'clock. Then, at 3 o'clock you're seeing the people from the bank. You're coming back on the 5.30 train.
WOMAN   Wow, that's quite a day!

Speaker 3   I'm spending Christmas with friends in Italy. I'm flying from Kennedy on Thursday 16th at 10.30am. I'm arriving in Milan at 9.45 in the evening. My friends are meeting me and driving me out to their home. I'm staying with them until Monday. Then I'm going to Rome for three days to do some sightseeing. I'm taking the train on Thursday 23rd to Venice where I'm staying with some other friends over the weekend. I'm returning to Milan by train on the Monday morning and flying home on the midday flight.

Lesson 3   Listening, activity 2

Speaker 1   One of us has to get up before the children wake up. It's usually my husband. Before hiding the chocolate eggs in the garden, he makes sure they're both asleep. After hiding them, he ties the dog up, so there are some left for the children! When they wake up, and before getting dressed, the children run into the garden and look for the eggs. Of course, they never find them all and my husband can never remember where he put them. So the dog does get his share. After eating all the chocolate eggs, they never want to eat the traditional Easter family lunch.

Speaker 2   In our home it is a fairy that comes and exchanges a tooth for a bit of money. After losing a tooth, the children put it under their pillow at bedtime. After they have gone to sleep, I carefully exchange the tooth for a coin. Of course, all sorts of things can go wrong. Sometimes we forget and have to think up an excuse for the fairy next day!

Speaker 3   For children, it is one of the most exciting times of year. Before going to bed, they put their stockings near the fireplace. During the night, after they have gone to bed, Father Christmas brings the presents and leaves them in the stockings. Next morning, before they have breakfast, the children open their presents. It is surprising how long children believe in Father Christmas. And they accept quite happily the idea of a big fat man coming down the chimney!

Lesson 4   Listening, activities 1 and 2

Speaker 1   I love riding. I was a lucky child because I lived on a farm and I had my first pony when I was eight. I haven't got a horse now, of course, because we live in the city. But I still go riding at least once a month. There's a place not too far away which isn't too expensive.

Speaker 2   I enjoy doing a lot of things in my spare time. But I really adore skiing. I don't go very often because I live in London now and it's terribly expensive, of course. I suppose I usually manage to get away, um, once a year. I always go with a group of friends and we stay in a chalet in the Alps. It's great fun.

Speaker 3   Well, I don't get very much spare time because I'm still studying. But I usually find time most afternoons to go for a walk in the park. I always feel so good when I get back to my books.

Speaker 4   I'm not very keen on sport. I prefer more relaxing activities like watching TV or listening to music. I especially enjoy playing cards with a group of friends. We get together every week for a meal and spend the rest of the evening playing cards. We usually play for a small amount of money which we put in a box and at the end of the year spend it on an evening out.

Lesson 7   Listening, activity 1

Speaker 1   I had a lonely childhood. I went to live with my uncle and his wife when I was five. They were very kind, but they didn't have any children of their own so they really didn't know how to cope with me. We lived on a farm several miles from the nearest village, and I used to feel very frustrated because, er, I couldn't play with the village children. Luckily, I enjoyed reading and I used to spend hours sitting in a tree reading adventure stories. I'm afraid those were the only really happy moments of my childhood.

Speaker 2   I think I was lucky in many ways. I lived in a small sea side village at a time when children could still play together in the village. Life used to be safer in those days and we were free and happy. We were also lucky to live by the sea and we used to spend hours swimming and going fishing. School doesn't take up much space in my memory. Life was one long holiday – or so it seems today!

Speaker 3   My parents were very musical; they both used to play in an orchestra, and my memories of childhood are mostly related to the world of music. We used to go to concerts every week, and I started to learn to play the piano when I was very small. We used to live in an enormous flat in the centre of London. It was so big that my brother and I used to ride our bicycles up and down the hall. We used to spend a lot of time indoors, but we were never bored. Our parents used to spend hours playing with us and we went on trips to the country most weekends.

Lesson 11   Listening, activity 1

Conversation 1
MRS E   Hello, Henry. I'm still at the airport. The plane was late. I'm going straight to the meeting. Has Ms Davidson phoned yet?
HENRY   No, she hasn't. Do you want me to contact her?
MRS E   No, that's all right. Um, have you prepared the report for the meeting this evening yet?
HENRY   Yes, I have. I've already sent it to your hotel.
MRS E   Oh, that's great. By the way. Don't worry about the mail. I can do it tomorrow.
HENRY   Oh, I've already done that. I posted it this morning. And I faxed Mr Brownlee.
MRS E   Oh, good. Right. I'd better go now. See you tomorrow, Henry.
HENRY   Goodbye, Mrs Evans.

Conversation 2
CALLER   Good afternoon. Could I speak to Mr James, please?
SEC.   I'm afraid, he hasn't come out of the meeting yet.

CALLER Oh, dear. I've already phoned three times today. It is really very important.

SEC. Well, I can't call him now, but I can ask him to phone you back as soon as he arrives.

CALLER Do you know what time his meeting ends?

SEC. Very soon. He still has a lot to do here in the office. Does he have your phone number?

CALLER No, he doesn't. It's 0982 32804. But I'm only here until four o'clock. Please tell him it is very important.

SEC. Yes, goodbye, Mr er ...

CALLER Heddon. Tony Heddon.

SEC. Goodbye, Mr Heddon.

CALLER Goodbye.

Lesson 16   Listening, activity 3

When I'm travelling, I generally behave in the same way as I do at home. Um, I'm always polite to the people I meet. And I don't think I deliberately provoke people. I certainly wouldn't kiss my boyfriend in public or wear a mini-skirt in the street. But wherever I go, I'm a Western woman and I don't pretend to be someone else. I mean, I don't see why I should wear a scarf over my head and a long dress just because that's the tradition in a particular country. When I travel, I generally wear jeans because that's what I find most comfortable. And if I'm in a very hot place, I wear shorts and sandals. If some people find that offensive, that's their problem, not mine. In some places, women are not expected to talk to men. Well, I think that's ridiculous. I behave in exactly the same way with both men and women as I do at home. I do try to avoid controversial topics of conversation. But, if someone else starts a discussion, I join in. I think it's good to speak your mind.

Lesson 21   Listening, activities 1 and 2

MAN Did you go out last night?

WOMAN Yes, I went to the cinema with some friends. We saw a really delightful film: *Four Weddings and a Funeral*. Have you been to see it?

MAN No, but I've been meaning to go.

WOMAN Oh, you really mustn't miss it. It's such a good film. A real breath of fresh air. No violence or anything like that. Just great entertainment. And a good laugh.

MAN Who are the main actors?

WOMAN Hugh Grant plays Charles an extremely handsome young gentleman. And he falls in love with Carrie, a terribly seductive American woman, played by Andie McDowell. There is a whole cast of absolutely brilliant actors who play the wedding guests. The first wedding scene is terribly funny. Charles is best man and when he gets to the church he's forgotten the rings, so he makes faces to a friend who passes him two other rings. We don't see the rings at first, but we can guess that they aren't right because the camera shows the priest's face when he sees them. The only scene that isn't funny is the funeral which is extremely emotional. And the ending is completely unexpected. Just when you think Charles is going to marry an ex-girlfriend, he...

MAN Don't tell me what happens. It'll only spoil the film for me.

Lesson 24   Listening, activities 1 and 2

MAN So, did you watch the sport last night?

WOMAN No. Why? Was it interesting?

MAN Yeah, it was the FA Cup. Yeah, Spurs won! And there was golf on as well, from St Andrews, which was good.

WOMAN Did they show the finals of the men's tennis?

MAN Oh, yes.

WOMAN Was it an exciting match? Who won?

MAN It was, er, André Agassi. Yeah, it was great. What did you watch?

WOMAN Oh, I watched that new soap. It's brilliant, and I'm really enjoying it. Did you see the first one?

MAN Yes, yes, I did. Yeah, it does look quite good. So, what was the second episode like?

WOMAN Frank wins the lottery, and ends up having a heart attack.

MAN Oh, wow. When's it on next?

WOMAN Erm, I think it's tomorrow night, I think it's about 8 o'clock.

MAN Oh, great.

WOMAN What are you doing this evening?

MAN I'm going to the cinema. And you?

WOMAN I'm going to watch TV again. There's, um, a brilliant wildlife programme on. I don't know if you've been watching it. It's really, really good. And then there's the news, of course. And, um, there's a documentary at 9. It's Panorama.

MAN Oh, yeah, that sounds really interesting.

WOMAN Do you want me to record the documentary for you?

MAN Yes, please.

WOMAN OK. There's a horror film on at midnight. I love horror films. Do you want me to record that, too?

MAN Um, what channel's it on?

WOMAN Er, um, BBC 2.

MAN Oh, OK. Yeah, there are no adverts. I just hate watching films that are interrupted by adverts.

WOMAN Oh, I'm the same. I hate them.

Lesson 26   Listening, activities 2 and 3

Speaker 1 Well, first of all, you put the bread rolls in the oven to heat. Now you must make sure the oven is not too hot because the rolls will dry up. Then we slice the tomatoes. Wash the lettuce. Now, very important, always dry the lettuce well because the bread will be soggy if, if it's still wet. Grill the burgers, or you can fry them in a heavy pan. Then you slice the cheese, and then it's time to take the warm rolls out of the oven. Open them up, place a slice of cheese on each piece of bread. And then you add the cooked burger meat. Then you put a slice of tomato and, of course, the lettuce leaf. Add tomato ketchup. Put the bread on the top. And then, of course, you serve them with chips and a nice glass of cold milk.

Speaker 2 OK, well, you need, um, a big mixing bowl and a wooden spoon. And, oh, you must make sure that you've put the oven on to heat. Um, and don't forget to warm the butter cos it has to be soft, OK? Right, mix the butter and sugar so you've got a nice creamy mixture. Um, you can use an electric beater if you've got one of those. And then add a spoonful of flour before the eggs. Right? Beat in the eggs very gradually. And never put them all in, you know, at the same time. Very gently add the flour. Make sure the mixture is creamy and nice and smooth. Er, you can add a little bit of milk if it's too thick. Now, put the chocolate in a pan and melt it. But very importantly, never boil the chocolate. OK? Right, then you pour the chocolate into the cake mixture. And fold it in with a spoon. And then you pour the mixture into the tin. Oh, don't forget to oil the baking tin, that's very important. Then you put it in the oven for about thirty minutes.

Speaker 3 Remember with this dish always to use fresh ingredients. Right, first you wash the lettuce. Dry it well, of course, and put it in a big bowl. Next, cut the avocado in half. Take the skin off, and discard that with the stone. And slice it thinly. Oh, don't forget to pour lemon juice on the avocado otherwise the slices will go black. Now we open the walnuts and spread them on the lettuce. Next, cut the blue cheese into small cubes and add them to the salad. Now, to prepare a dressing. You can use either walnut or sunflower oil. But we never use olive oil with walnuts; it makes them taste funny. Give the dressing a good stir, and pour it onto the salad. Um, toss the salad just before serving and there you are.

Lesson 27   Listening

Speaker 1 Let me think. What do I really hate? Oh, I know. People who come and sit down right next to me when I'm lying on the beach. I really can't stand that, especially when there are a few people on the beach. I mean, I usually get up and move somewhere else.

Speaker 2 When I'm travelling about there are a number of things that I find annoying. I get really angry with taxi drivers who think they own the road. They drive well over the speed limit and then curse at other people for going too slowly. And I can't stand smiling airline staff who happily tell you that your plane will be half a day late. I can never understand why they look so happy.

Speaker 3 When I go on holiday, I'm a bit fussy about the hotel. I don't mind if it's old-fashioned or not very smart, but I have to have a bathroom. I really hate hotels where the toilets are at the end of the corridor. Another thing I don't like is a room which doesn't have an interesting view. I don't mind if it's a busy street, but I like to have something to look at. I always check these details when I book the hotel so that I'm not disappointed.

Speaker 4 One thing I find really annoying are magazine and newspaper articles that encourage people to go to beautiful unspoilt places. How can a place remain unspoilt when thousands of people read about it in a popular magazine? Then, of course, you go to these places and discover that they are full of tourists. When I'm on holiday I hate having to send postcards. I never know what to write. And I don't like receiving cards that I can't read. That's very frustrating.

Lesson 29   Listening, activity 1

Speaker 1 Oh, no, no, we never take our cars to the garage. I mean, we do everything ourselves. I mean, I wouldn't dream of having a car repaired by a mechanic. It just costs so much money, you know, for the labour. The only thing we won't do is clean the car. I mean, I hate doing it. We get our younger brother to take it to an automatic car wash. We do pay him to do it.

Speaker 2 Um, I do most routine things myself, like, um, I check the water level, er, the, um, pressure in the tyres and, and of course the oil. But, um, I get a mechanic to do any repair work and, um, I get my husband to clean it on Saturdays.

Speaker 3 Well, I don't do anything myself at all. I, er, I did actually have to change a tyre once in an emergency, but I, ugh, I wouldn't do it again, it was a horrible experience, very very dirty. Um, I can't stand anything to do with cars. Um, people who's job it is, I mean, that's fine for them, but I, I really don't enjoy it at all. I always, er, get a professional mechanic to do any repairs. I, er, I get a service station attendant to check my tyres and oil and the battery thing as well. And, er, I also have it cleaned there as well. I mean, I, obviously I pay them to do it, but I wouldn't do it myself.

Lesson 31 Listening, activities 2 and 3

MAN I find going on holiday terribly tiring. I sometimes wonder if it's worth all the worry and stress. By the time I've got everything ready, I'm so exhausted I, I need a holiday just to recover from all the preparations.

WOMAN Aren't you exaggerating a bit?

MAN No, not at all. To start with, there are all the things that can go wrong at home when you're away. I, I always leave my address with the neighbours so they can contact me in an emergency. And I never leave anything valuable in the house. That would just be asking for it.

WOMAN I never worry about things like that. I take out a good insurance policy in case the house gets burgled. I do give the neighbour a key, though, in case there's a power cut. One year when I went away the electricity was off for ten days and everything in the deep freeze went rotten.

MAN Then there's the problem of foreign currency. When I go abroad I only carry traveller's cheques. At least you can get your money back if your bag is stolen.

WOMAN Oh, I never bother with traveller's cheques. You have to order them from the bank; it's such a nuisance. I just take a credit card and some foreign currency in case the exchange bureaux are shut. I've always found that most places accept cards nowadays.

MAN Another thing I worry about is missing planes. I'm frightened of flying as it is, but I'm even more scared of missing the plane. You never know when you will arrive if you get stuck in heavy traffic, and you can't even rely on the trains these days, they're always on strike. So what I do now is spend the night at the airport.

WOMAN What in the airport lounge?

MAN Well, only if it's a morning flight. Otherwise, I go to a hotel.

WOMAN Well, I certainly wouldn't go that far. But I have nearly missed the plane once or twice when the traffic was really bad. So what I do now is try to leave for the airport an hour or so early in case something goes wrong on the way there. Then I take a good book in case I get there too early and have a long wait.

MAN Then when I get to where I'm going there are all sorts of things which are such a nuisance. Insects are the worst. I have to take insect repellent cream to keep them away, and sleeping tablets so the noise they make doesn't keep me awake. It's not much fun at all. In fact, I need at least two packets of aspirins because I get such bad headaches with all the extra worry.

WOMAN It sounds as if you would have a better holiday if you stayed at home!

Lesson 32 Listening, activities 2 and 3

Conversation 1

WOMAN Good morning. I'm phoning about a television I bought from you last week. I'm afraid there's something wrong with it.

ASST. Oh, what exactly is the matter?

WOMAN Well, when I switched it on the first time, the picture was fine but there was no sound. So I turned it off and checked the plug and the aerial. Then I turned it on again and this time the sound was all right, but there was no picture.

ASST. Well, how strange! Er, you've got the receipt, have you?

WOMAN Oh, yes. And the guarantee.

ASST. Right. Then, I'll send the technician round to have a look at

it as soon as he has finished with a customer. Could you give me your name and address, please.

WOMAN Er, Mrs Simpson, Number 14 Water Road. When do you think he's likely to come?

ASST. It is most likely to be this afternoon. Would you like us to phone you?

WOMAN No, that won't be necessary, I'll be in all day. Thank you. Goodbye.

ASST. Goodbye

Conversation 2

ASST. Can I help you, sir?

MAN Yeah. It's about a kitchen cupboard kit I bought from you on Saturday. It's impossible to assemble the drawers because there are several bits missing from the box.

ASST. Hmm. Have you got it with you?

MAN No. I spent the whole weekend trying to put it together and I haven't taken it apart again. I wondered if you could give me the pieces that are missing. I've got the list here.

ASST. Oh, I'm afraid that's not possible. We can exchange the kit for another one but we can't provide parts. You'll have to take it apart and bring it in.

MAN That's crazy! And in any case there are bits of wood which have been glued together. It's impossible to get them apart without damaging the cupboard.

ASST. Oh. Have you got the receipt with you?

MAN Yes, of course.

ASST. All right. I'll explain the problem to the manager when he comes in. He is expected to arrive at about three thirty, so if you phone round about four you're sure to get him.

MAN Thank you. Goodbye.

ASST. Goodbye.

Conversation 3

ASST. Can I help you, sir?

MAN Yes, you certainly can. It's this radio.

ASST. Is there something wrong with it?

MAN I only bought it last week and when I took it out of the box, I found that the volume button didn't work and the aerial was broken. It's disgraceful to sell things that haven't been properly checked.

ASST. I'm terribly sorry, sir. We do usually check all our electrical goods before the customer takes them away. Didn't the person who sold it to you test it?

MAN They certainly did not! It's a disgrace! Either you repair it or you exchange it for one that works properly.

ASST. Yes, of course. Could I see your receipt, please?

MAN What do you mean? What receipt?

ASST. The receipt you were given when you paid for the radio. I'm afraid, I can't do anything for you if you haven't kept the receipt.

MAN That's ridiculous! You don't need a receipt to tell that the thing's broken. I don't know where it is, anyway.

ASST. Well, I'll be pleased to help you when you have found the receipt, but until then, I'm afraid, I can't do very much for you, sir.

MAN I shall complain to the police!

Conversation 4

WOMAN My name is Jean Phelps. I'm phoning about my washing machine. You came round yesterday afternoon to look at the machine. You said you thought it would be all right, but it isn't. It's still leaking all over the floor when it's on rinse.

MAN Well, it must be the pump after all. I'll have to change it, but unfortunately I haven't got a spare one in the workshop at the moment.

WOMAN Oh, dear. Well, I can't manage without the machine. When do you expect to be able to do it?

MAN We are due to receive spare parts for that particular make sometime next week.

WOMAN I can't possibly wait that long. Can't you exchange the machine for another one that isn't faulty? It doesn't seem right to have to pay so much money for something that doesn't work!

MAN No, I'm afraid that isn't possible. But I can lend you a second-hand machine until I get the parts.

WOMAN Well, that'll be OK. When are you likely to be able to bring it round?

MAN I'll send the delivery van round as soon as it gets in. That should be before twelve.

WOMAN That's fine. Thank you very much.

Lesson 36 Listening, activities 1 and 2

Conversation 1

MAN You look tired, Mary. Have you had a night out?

MARY I wish I had. It's my husband, Paul; he snores so loudly he keeps me awake most of the night. It's the sort of thing I'd laugh about if it wasn't such a nuisance.

MAN Have you talked to him about it?

MARY I've tried to, but he won't listen. He says I'm exaggerating. So, what do I do now? I've tried kicking him. I've tried pouring water in his ear. He just turns over and carries on snoring. It's driving me mad.

MAN Yes, I can see your problem. Well, if I were you, I'd talk to his doctor about it and see what he can suggest.

MARY Yes, that's probably the best thing to do. At least he can give me some sleeping tablets, if nothing else.

Conversation 2

WOMAN Are you off on another trip, Pete?

PETE Yes, I'm going to Japan to negotiate a big sales deal.

WOMAN Oh, that sounds exciting. How long will you be staying?

PETE That's the problem. I can only spend three days there because I have to be back for the company's annual general meeting on the fourth.

WOMAN Oh, that's a bit short, isn't it?

PETE Yes. I'm very worried about how I'll cope with the negotiations if I'm jet-lagged.

WOMAN Perhaps you ought to leave a few days earlier so you can recover before you start work.

PETE I'm afraid I can't. Everything's been booked.

WOMAN Well, in that case, you should at least avoid alcoholic drinks and heavy meals.

Conversation 3

MAN Goodness! What have you done to your hair? It's orange!

WOMAN Oh, don't remind me. I'm terribly upset. I went to that new salon that's just opened on the High Street. I only asked the stupid girl for a shampoo and a trim and this is what she did. I thought it was taking rather a long time, but I didn't realise she was dyeing it orange! It'll take ages to grow out.

MAN Oh, well, I suppose it could have been green!

WOMAN Oh, shut up! You're a great help!

MAN Sorry. That was mean of me. I think it's a disgrace. You should complain to the management.

WOMAN I've already done that and it hasn't helped a bit.

MAN Oh, well, in that case you should contact a lawyer and ask for advice.

Lesson 37 Listening, activity 1

Conversation 1

WOMAN Where did you spend August this year, Henry?

MAN I went to St Tropez on the French Riviera with some friends. We stayed at a campsite just outside the town.

WOMAN Oh, yes. I know St Tropez very well. I used to spend the summer there when I was younger. A beautiful place and so authentic. A typical French fishing village.

MAN Well, I don't know about a fishing village. There were certainly a lot of luxury yachts on the harbour front, but their owners didn't seem to be fishing for anything other than attention. It was amazing the number of elegant people everywhere. Even their bikinis looked as though they'd been designed by Chanel. It was a bit of a surprise at first because we hadn't expected it to be so busy. But we had a good time all the same. It was fun watching all those rich people showing off!

WOMAN Oh, well, you should have seen it in my day. Such a sweet little place. That was before it was ruined by tourists. But I believe it is still quite pleasant out of season, in May or September. Anyway, you enjoyed yourself, which is the main thing.

Conversation 2

MAN Oh, you're back then. Did you have a good time? Budapest, was it?

WOMAN Yes, that's right. It was great. I'm not sure I'd go in January again, though. It was pretty cold. I hadn't really expected it to be freezing in the daytime, and I had to buy gloves and a fur hat which helped a bit. It was very spectacular, though. Especially when it snowed and all the beautiful old buildings were covered in snow.

MAN When is the best time to go, would you say?

WOMAN It's probably sensible to avoid the peak tourist season in the summer. May or early June is probably a good time. That's when I'd go if I were doing the trip again.

MAN What was your accommodation like? Did you manage to find somewhere decent and not too pricey?

WOMAN It wasn't too bad. A bit far from the centre, that was the only problem. I asked at the airport information centre when I arrived and they gave me the name of the hotel. Apparently it's better to book through a travel agent before you leave. You get lower prices and they know which places are the best value for money. I'd certainly do it that way if I was going again. Oh, and I'd take a good winter coat and snow boots if I had to go in the winter!

Conversation 3

MAN You're not looking very well. Don't you think you need a holiday?

WOMAN Don't mention holidays. I've just got back from a disastrous week on the Spanish coast.

MAN Oh, dear, what went wrong?

WOMAN Everything. Things started badly when the car broke down on the way to the airport and I nearly missed the flight. Now, I wish I had missed it, though. It would have saved a lot of trouble.

MAN That was unlucky. You should have caught the train. It's always more reliable. What happened next?

WOMAN Well, I put my hand luggage down on a bench while I went to check-in my suitcase ...

MAN Oh, don't tell me. It was stolen. That was a really stupid thing to do in a public place. I hope you had traveller's cheques and not much cash.

WOMAN You must be joking. I had mostly cash. Luckily, I did have a hundred pound's worth of traveller's cheques, but of course I'd forgotten to note down their numbers, and it was a real hassle to sort out!

MAN You seem to have done everything wrong so far. What happened next?

WOMAN The first day on the beach I stayed on the beach all day and got so sunburnt I couldn't go out in the sun again for the rest of the holiday. Then, I drank water from a street fountain and spent two days in bed ill. I still haven't recovered. The doctor has just given me a week off work.

MAN Oh, well, it certainly was a disaster!

Lesson 39 Listening, activity 1

Speaker 1 I had a wonderful childhood. I liked school, although I, I can't say I worked very hard. Looking back, I can see that I was lucky. I went to one of those old-fashioned prep schools where there were only about 30 pupils and the headmistress was a kindly old lady who used to read us boarders stories before we went to bed. I don't have many regrets. I sometimes wish I'd worked a bit harder when I moved on to my local comprehensive school, though. I had a good time there too. Sport was my favourite subject, of course. But I failed all my exams and had to spend a year redoing them at technical college, which wasn't much fun. I studied economics which hasn't really been very useful to me. I gave up languages quite early which was a mistake. I had to take evening classes later on.

Speaker 2 I had a really miserable time at primary school. It was a dreadful village school with a terrifying headmaster who used to frighten me terribly. I'm sure I'd have been happier at a boarding school. I was a good worker, so I didn't get into much trouble. Then I moved on to the high school. I worked extremely hard there and passed my exams quite easily. My parents were pleased, of course, but I always regret not having a good time like the other girls. They used to talk about their evenings out on the town and films they'd been to see. I used to be very envious. I wouldn't want my children to have the same experience of school.

Speaker 3 Oh, it wasn't so bad. I went to a public school. I wasn't a boarder, though, I used to go in on the bus every day. My favourite subjects were music and history and they've both been very useful to me in my career. I chose Latin instead of Spanish or Italian which was a mistake. But, of course, you don't realise at the time you make these decisions. I still can't understand Spanish, which is an awful nuisance because I travel such a lot. I regret not learning to play a musical instrument. I'm the only person in the family who doesn't play anything. Unfortunately, I can't even sing! The only thing I hated about school was all the homework we got. It just didn't seem fair to have to work all day and then start again in the evening. Even my parents didn't have to do that! I certainly won't let my children spend all their spare time doing school work.

Answer Key

Lesson 1
VOCABULARY AND SOUNDS
1 & 2 *Example answers*
Classroom: <u>a</u>loud, <u>a</u>nswer, complete, ex<u>plain</u>, mis<u>take</u>, pro<u>nounce</u>, re<u>peat</u>
Private life: <u>a</u>ddress, <u>children</u>, married, single
Others: fluent, foreign, journey
3 1 married 2 children 3 fluent; foreign 4 abroad 5 journey
FUNCTIONS
1 1 f 2 e 3 h 4 g 5 c 6 b 7 a 8 d
2 1 <u>What</u> <u>do</u> <u>next</u> 2 <u>explain</u> <u>again</u> <u>please</u> 3 <u>repeat</u> <u>please</u> 4 <u>What</u> <u>page</u> <u>on</u> 5 <u>What's</u> English 'bon appétit' 6 <u>How</u> <u>spell</u> 'answer' 7 <u>speak</u> <u>slowly</u> <u>please</u> 8 <u>What</u> 'function'
GRAMMAR
1 2 Were 3 Did 4 Do 5 Did 6 Have 7 Are 8 Did
3 2 How 3 Why 4 Who 5 What 6 Where 7 When 8 Who
LISTENING
1 *Example answers* b What do you do? *or* What is your job? c Is your job dangerous? d What do you miss most about Australia? e Have you been back to Australia? f Why did you come to live in Britain? g Do you travel a lot?
2 1 a 2 f 3 b 4 c 5 g 6 e 7 d
3 1, 3, 5 and 7.

Lesson 2
VOCABULARY
plane: boarding pass, baggage retrieval, cabin, charter check in, crew, customs, departure lounge, duty-free, flight, ground staff, passport control, take off terminal, transfer area train: compartment, platform, waiting room both: announcement, arrivals, catch, connection, crowd, delay, fare, information desk, passenger, reservation
GRAMMAR
1 *Example answers*
2 He/she searches passengers' baggage. 3 He/she serves drinks. 4 He/she flies the plane. 5 He/she weighs passengers' baggage.
6 He/she carries suitcases.
2 *Example answers* 2 The airline check-in clerk is checking passengers' tickets and weighing their luggage.
3 The passport control officer is checking passports. 4 The passenger is waiting in the departure lounge to board a flight to Hong Kong.
3 1 is having 2 don't understand 3 works 4 land; take off 5 studies; is working 6 spends; is flying 7 like
8 am leaving; am attending
9 drink 10 doesn't want

LISTENING
1 b e
2 Speaker 1: Vancouver by plane
Speaker 2: Boston by train
Speaker 3: Italy by plane then around Italy by car and train.
Speaker 2: is travelling for business
3 Read the tapescript and check your answers.

Lesson 3
VOCABULARY
1 groom 2 veil 3 horoscope
4 ceremonies 5 registry office
6 celebrating
READING
2 A poet and musicians entertain the wedding guests.
3 1 e 2 g 3 f 4 c 5 a 6 b 7 d
4 1 The farmers grow corn which they sell at the end of the summer. 2 Important.
3 They give traditional presents.
4 Important.
5 They give him something to eat and drink.
GRAMMAR
1 during the 'night of the henna'; during the day; during the narrative; during the presentation; for several hours
2 1 the farmers have sold the summer harvest 2 greeting the poet 3 he takes refreshments
4 having an early supper
5 praying at the mosque
3 2 After the bride's hands and feet have been painted with henna, the wedding festivities can begin. 3 After the poet has had a sleep, he tunes his instruments. 4 After the guests have taken their seats, the poet appears on the platform. 5 After the wedding ceremony has taken place, the bride's family present her trousseau.
LISTENING
1, 2 & 3 Speaker 1: Sentences 2 5 7 – Easter Sunday Speaker 2: Sentences 4 6 – the tooth fairy Speaker 3: Sentences 1 3 8 – Christmas

Lesson 4
VOCABULARY
1 Positive: brilliant, entertaining, exciting, fun, great, relaxing, superb, terrific, wonderful
Negative: awful, boring, dreadful, dull, terrible, frightening
GRAMMAR
1 1 c 2 d 3 a 4 e 5 b
2 2 He enjoys watching the football on television every Saturday night. 3 I go away on holiday twice a year.
4 They hardly ever entertain friends at their home. 5 She goes cycling in the park most mornings. 6 We never take the children to the cinema.

SOUNDS
2 <u>really</u> <u>hate</u> <u>staying</u> <u>in</u> <u>so</u> <u>bored</u>
3 <u>enjoy</u> <u>gardening</u> <u>don't</u> <u>collecting</u> <u>leaves</u> 4 <u>can't</u> <u>stand</u> <u>cleaning</u> <u>house</u> <u>dull</u> <u>work</u>
5 <u>mind</u> <u>staying</u> <u>home</u> <u>children</u>
READING
1 A 4; B 2
2 A: winners, bet, draw, temptation, chance, lottery number, luck
B: orderly, push, bus-stop, wait, stand, patiently
3 national lottery, cock-fighting, fish-fighting, boxing
4 humorous
LISTENING
1 & 2 Read the tapescript and check your answers.

Lesson 5
VOCABULARY
1 delighted, excited, frightened, puzzled, surprised
They end in *-ed*.
2 2 embarrassing 3 frightened
4 surprised 5 amazing
6 delighted
3 2 Opera isn't interesting.
3 Rock music is exciting.
4 Watching television is relaxing. 5 Politics is boring.
READING
1 2
2 local politics: interested annoyed
personal relationships: embarrassed
travel: relaxed
football: excited
3 world news: depressing
money: embarrassing
music: exciting
SOUNDS
1 2 & 3
1 are we? A unhappy
2 aren't you? Q impatient
3 don't you? Q friendly
4 is it? A bored
5 do you? A angry
6 isn't it? A polite

Lesson 6
VOCABULARY
1 & 2 ambition, ambitious, unambitious confidence, confident, unconfident honesty, honest, dishonest idealism, idealistic, realistic independence, independent, dependent intelligence, intelligent, unintelligent patience, patient, impatient reliability, reliable, unreliable sincerity, sincere, insincere talent, talented, untalented
READING
1 A He went to meet him in his dressing room. B They met at a party. C They met hiking in Scotland. D They met in his dressing room. E They met in the mountains.
2 A talented, open, down-to-earth manner, sense of humour
B dreamer, solitary,

understanding C patience, self-control, determination, optimist, extrovert D None mentioned.
E kind, shy
3 A and D are friends; C and E are friends; B is the odd one out.
GRAMMAR
1 2 She stayed with a friend.
3 They were working hard.
4 We didn't live here.
5 I wasn't listening.
2 1 was playing; saw 2 were fighting; arrived 3 were travelling 4 met; was working 5 came; were staying 6 was writing; died
3 I wasn't feeling very happy. I was taking a group into the mountains. I was working away from home.
4 2 was hiking in Scotland
3 was wearing a fashionable, black overcoat 4 was studying

Lesson 7
VOCABULARY
1 prize 2 behave 3 trip
4 competitions 5 outings
6 neighbours
READING
1 happy
2 It was by the sea. There were a lot of holidaymakers in the summer. It was a fishing village. There was a harbour.
3 She used to devour enormous slices of bread and jam. She used to jump off the harbour wall. She used to watch the speed boats. She used to go fishing off the rocks. She used to spend hours in rock pools.
4 2 I used to live in a little seaside village. 3 We used to run free. 4 We used to jump off the harbour wall. 5 The young people used to drive speed boats around the bay.
6 They didn't use to mix with us locals. 7 We used to follow the rhythm of the sea.
5 1
LISTENING
1 Speaker 1: unhappy
Speaker 2: happy
Speaker 3: happy
2 Speaker 2
3 Read the tapescript and check your answers.

Lesson 8
GRAMMAR
1 2 I reached the station
3 she arrived in Rome
4 the traffic lights turned green
5 he realised he was lost
6 I waited at the information desk
2 2 While 3 when 4 when
5 as *or* when 6 as
3 2 While they were waiting at reception, the police were searching the room. When the police were searching the room,

they were waiting at reception.
3 I was feeling very lonely
when my friend called me. My
friend called me while I was
feeling very lonely.
4 A group of people crowded
round us as we were standing
in a queue. When we were
standing in a queue, a group of
people crowded round us.
5 He stood up when the teacher
walked into the room.
As soon as the teacher walked
into the room, he stood up.
6 I had to wait for an hour
while they checked my
passport. I had to wait for an
hour until they checked my
passport.
4 1 was eating; took
2 announced; were flying
3 looked out; saw   4 stopped;
told   5 was checking
6 touched   7 landed; pushed
8 arrived; were serving

READING
1 3
2 1 after *tied to the quayside*
2 after *got out our fishing lines*
3 after *because of the pain*
4 after *chugged sadly
homewards*
3 2 He was very shaken.
3 They were sad.   4 He was
puzzled and alarmed.
5 They were worried.
6 They were relieved.

Lesson 9
GRAMMAR
1 1 which   2 which   3 who
4 who   5 which
2 1 Coffee, which came from the
Middle East, was common in
most of Europe by the 17th
century.   2 Brazil, which
occupies nearly half the
continent, is the largest South
American country.   3 Budapest,
which is on the Danube, is the
capital of Hungary.   4 Picasso,
who died in Paris in 1973,
influenced may modern
painters.   5 Conan Doyle, who
was a 19th-century English
author, created the detective
Sherlock Holmes.
3 2 Columbus, who was Italian,
reached America in 1492.
Columbus, who reached
America in 1492, was Italian.
3 Cervantes, who lived in the
16th century, wrote *Don
Quixote*. Cervantes, who wrote
Don Quixote, lived in the 16th
century.   4 Walt Disney, who
created Mickey Mouse, began
his career in 1920. Walt Disney,
who began his career in 1920,
created Mickey Mouse.   5
Rotterdam, which is on the
North Sea, is the world's largest
port. Rotterdam, which is the
world's largest port, is on the

North Sea.   6 Tea, which
requires a warm climate, is
grown in India and China. Tea,
which is grown in India and
China, requires a warm climate.
READING
1 1
2 *Example answers* He is a chef.
He worked for Gaston Lenôtre.
He runs a restaurant. He is a
'nose'. He has written a book
about chocolate. He has started
a chocolate club. He is a hard
worker. He is a chocolate
addict.
3 Constant, who is a chef, admits
that... the restaurant he
opened last month, which is in
the style of the 1930s...
Constant explains that the
mouth, which can only taste
four things... But Columbus,
who disliked the odd bitter
taste... Constant, who is a hard
worker...
4 The club, which already has
over 150 members, is called The
Chocolate Munchers.
During the day the restaurant,
which only serves full meals in
the evenings, is a chocolate
tearoom...
...in 1502 Christopher
Columbus, who was lost in a
storm, came across an island
and went ashore.
5 taste: spicy, bitter, flavour,
sweet, acid
The extra words refer to smell.

SOUNDS
fasci**na**tion	**fasci**nate (✘)
prepa**ra**tion	**pre**pare (✘)
expla**na**tion	ex**plain** (✘)
deco**ra**tion	**deco**rate (✘)
se**lec**tion	se**lect** (✔)
cre**a**tion	cre**ate** (✔)
organi**sa**tion	**organ**ise (✘)

Lesson 10
SOUNDS
2 1 f (?)   2 a (✔)   3 c (✘)
4 e (✘)   5 b (✘)   6 d (✔)
3 a polite   b polite   c impolite
d polite   e polite   f impolite

GRAMMAR AND FUNCTIONS
1 lend, take, give and tell
show, make, send, pass
2 2 They showed her photos of
their home.   3 He sold the
company ten computers.
4 We gave our hostess a bunch
of flowers.   5 He offered the
elderly gentleman a seat.
6 I read my children a story.
3 *Example answers* 2 Could you
pass me the salt and pepper,
please?   3 Could you send me
a brochure?   4 Would you
mind ordering me a taxi?
5 Could you show me the
report, please?   6 Would you
mind taking her some
magazines, please?

VOCABULARY
1 feelings: angry, anxious, bored,
cross, embarrassed, hurt,
pleased, surprised, worried
behaviour: casual, dishonest,
friendly, immoral, mean, polite,
reluctant
READING
1 greetings and gift-giving
2 1 In France, kissing is a
common form of greeting
between close friends and
relatives.   2 German hospitality
is very formal.   3 There are no
specific rules for greetings in
Greece.   4 They are not
acceptable as they are
reminders of death.
3 *Example answers* 1 You should
take your Greek hostess flowers
or a cake.   2 You can give a
French person flowers,
chocolates or something
intellectual or aesthetic.
3 A man should offer a German
hostess an odd number of
flowers (but not red roses).

Lesson 11
VOCABULARY
throw away the rubbish, do the
washing up, make the lunch, lay
the table, tidy up the house,
clean the cooker, turn on the
heating, put out the cat
GRAMMAR
1 2 Have you booked the theatre
tickets yet?   3 Are you still
interested in archaeology?
4 They have already met the
new student.   5 They still
haven't found their dog.
6 She hasn't arrived at the office
yet.
2 left; cleared; done; gone; been;
drawn; thrown away; drunk;
taken out; put on; brought; had;
found; tidied
3 already; yet; already; yet; still;
still; yet; still
4 2 She hasn't bought it yet.
3 She's already collected the
present.   4 She's still tidying up
the dining room.   5 She's
already prepared the bedrooms.
6 She hasn't cooked the meal
yet.
7 He has already come.
LISTENING
1 Conversation 1: They know
each other.   Conversation 2:
They are strangers.
2 1 ✘   2 ✔   3 ✔   4 ✔   5 ✔
3 1 Mr James hasn't come out of
the meeting yet.
2 Mr Heddon has already
phoned three times.
3 Mr James hasn't finished his
work at the office yet.
SOUNDS
1 2 No, they haven't finished it
yet.   3 No, she hasn't seen it
yet.   4 No, they haven't bought
one yet.   5 No, he hasn't tidied
it up yet.

Lesson 12
VOCABULARY
1 *Example answers* Photo A:
crew, ,drown, forecast, gale, sea,
helicopter, rescue, sink, storm,
weather, wind
Photo B: burn, chaos, destroy,
evacuate, firefighters, heat,
rescue, smoke, temperature,
volunteers, wind
2 1 seas; rescue; helicopter; crew;
drowned; sink
2 smoke; burn; volunteers;
firefighters; temperature; winds;
evacuating
GRAMMAR
1 2 The band has been playing
for three hours.   3 The dollar
has been rising since March.
4 They have been sailing since
last June.
2 2 How long has the band been
playing?   3 How long has the
dollar been rising?   4 How long
have they been sailing?
READING
1 1 B   2 C   3 A
2 they have been testing a saucer;
helicopters have been lifting;
some individuals have been
living on the island
3 for: at least a year, up to 200
years   since: Monday, 1835,
then (last month)
4 1 They have been
experimenting with flying
saucers for many years.
2 They have been fighting the
fire for 13 days.   3 The police
have trying to trace the missing
painting for a month.
SOUNDS
1 areas, chaos, evacuate,
desperate, destroy, rescue,
reward, species, volunteer
2 nightfall, neighbouring, know
design, fighting, island, weigh

Lesson 13
VOCABULARY
1 nouns: cartoon, character,
comic, delight, film, heroine,
laugh, movie, novel, pet, series
adjectives: brave, comic, evil,
famous, fictional, latest,
popular, successful
verbs: appear, conquer, delight,
film, laugh, save
2 1 appeared; cartoon
2 successful; series
3 latest; evil   4 laugh; famous
5 successful; heroine
READING
1 Tintin and Asterix
2 Hergé, the Belgian cartoonist,
died in 1983 but Tintin, his
creation, lives on. The brave
young reporter made his first
big trip on January 10th 1929 to
the USSR. His next trip was to
the Congo in 1931 and then to

the US in 1932. Since he started his career as a journalist he has visited more than 30 different countries all over the world and has even landed on the moon. He has been solving mysteries and getting out of sticky situations with his faithful dog Snowy for over 60 years. He has even appeared in a number of films. The first full-length cartoon of his adventures in Egypt was made in 1969. Since then children and adults from all over the world and speaking over 30 different languages have been following the fantastic adventures of this brave young man.

GRAMMAR
1 **present perfect continuous:**
The brave warrior and his big friend Obelix have been delighting millions of comic-reading children for more than 30 years.   He has been solving mysteries and getting out of sticky situations with his faithful dog Snowy for over 60 years. Since then children and adults from all over the world and speaking 30 different languages have been following the fantastic adventures of this brave young man.
present perfect simple:
Asterix the Gaul has conquered most of the world.   Since he started his career as a journalist, he has visited more than 30 countries.   He has even landed on the moon.
162 million people have seen the six cartoon films set in Roman times that have been made to date.   He has even appeared in a number of films.
2 a The sentences in the present perfect simple.
b The sentences in the present perfect continuous.
3 2 I have been travelling for over six hours.   3 He has smoked more than ten cigarettes since two o'clock.
4 He has been trying to give up smoking for ages.   5 We have bought a new, red sports car.
6 She has appeared in two popular television series.
4 1 have been studying   2 have studied   3 has been living   4 has lived   5 have been acting   6 have acted   7 has been appearing   8 has appeared
5 how long: 1, 3, 5 and 7
how many: 2, 4, 6 and 8
How long have you been studying English?   How long has she been living in Rome?   How many tenses have you studied?   How many flats has she lived in?

SOUNDS
2 seen last week   3 worked two different companies
4 met sister Anna?
5 appearing TV series long
6 just bought new house suburbs

Lesson 14
VOCABULARY
1 Buildings and architecture: bridge, concrete, cathedral, landmark, fountain, square, picturesque, church, baroque, modern, dirty, palace, skyline, industrial, vertical, suburb, low, gothic, town hall, tall, tower block, glass, big Atmosphere: noisy, romantic, lively, exciting, old-fashioned, sophisticated, busy, sleepy, dangerous, wealthy, smart, cosmopolitan

GRAMMAR
1 1 cheaper   2 bigger   3 shorter   4 more crowded   5 further
2 2 It rains more in Riga than in Naples.   3 There are fewer inhabitants in Riga than in Naples.   4 Riga is further north than Naples.   5 There are fewer tourists during the summer in Riga than in Naples.   6 Hotels are more expensive in Riga than in Naples.

SOUNDS
1 romantic   2 hall   3 square   4 low   5 lively

READING
1 a travel guide
2 Yes
3 the cemetery: magical, lonely, increasingly popular, hidden spots
the architecture: grandiose, colourful, Italian, bigger and better, Venice for giants
4 ...as good as the over-familiar tourist attractions...   The most beautiful time of year...
...one of the world's grandest cities.   ...to make buildings bigger and better than anywhere else...   You feel, smell and experience life more vividly here than in any other European city.
5 mostly the writer's impressions

Lesson 15
VOCABULARY
1 necklace, armchair, briefcase spotlight, wristwatch, sunglasses, grandfather hairbrush, ashtray
2 1 wood   2 short   3 interesting   4 transparent   5 leather   6 Spanish

GRAMMAR
1 2 An expensive, multi-coloured, silk carpet.   3 A set of magnificent, 17th-century, Venetian glasses.
4 A fashionable, black, lycra cycling-suit.   5 An attractive, modern, gold watch.
2 telephone 3   leather jacket 6

watch 1   bicycle 4   sunglasses 5   jeans 2
3 1 elegant; delicate
2 popular; well-known
3 old-fashioned; valuable
4 well-balanced; comfortable
5 fashionable; amusing
6 comfortable
4 1 My; yours   2 our; yours
3 mine; hers   4 her; mine
5 my; Yours

READING
1 positive
2 1 true   2 false   3 true   4 true   5 false
3 wooden, rubber, hollow, plastic, more stable, more visible, safer, elegant, light, heavy, recycled, stackable, benevolent, successful
Elegant and *benevolent* express opinions.
4 1 b   2 b   3 a   4 a   5 b

Lesson 16
GRAMMAR
1 1 You shouldn't look people in the eyes.   2 In Japan, you are supposed to exchange business cards before starting work.
3 Do you have to arrive on time at meetings in Latin America?
4 Am I supposed to offer to pay for the meal?   5 Am I supposed to offer to take business associates home?
2 Germany 2; Spain 4; France 3 Britain 1

READING
1 Social behaviour in South Korea
2 1 You should never offer to pay for yourself.   2 If you invite people out, you are supposed to pay the bill.
3 The person who invites should pay.   4 A man should always pay for a woman.

LISTENING
2 Accept other countries as they are and respect their traditions. Don't impose your own cultural behaviour. Try to adapt to the customs of the country you are visiting. Avoid wearing clothes that may shock people.
3 The speaker doesn't agree with all the advice in the passage.
4 behaviour, clothes, bare legs (shorts), controversial topics and kissing in public.
5 *Example answers*
You should avoid eye contact with strange men. You should wear sunglasses. You should carry family photos. You shouldn't wear provocative clothes. You should cover your hair with a scarf. You shouldn't show bare legs. You should avoid controversial topics of conversation. You shouldn't kiss in public.

Lesson 17
GRAMMAR
Certain: 2 5 8   Probable: 1 6 Possible: 3 4 7

SOUNDS
2 I'm sure you won't see him tomorrow.   3 I'm sure you will have time to meet me this evening.   4 I'm sure she won't stay for the weekend.   5 I'm sure you will go back to the studio this evening.   6 I'm sure she won't be late.   7 I'm sure they won't remember to call and see us.   8 I'm sure he won't stay in this evening.

READING
2 he might smoke, he might read, he might leave the light on, he might snore
3 I'm sure he won't smoke because he's never smoked in his life. I'm sure he won't read because he is tired. I'm sure he won't leave the light on because he wants to get some sleep. I'm sure he won't snore because he never does.
4 impatient, impolite, insensitive, inconsiderate
Example answers
writer: patient, polite
stranger: intolerant, impolite
5 3

Lesson 18
VOCABULARY
1 demanding, enjoyable, exciting, fun, glamorous interesting, repetitive, rewarding, tiring

SOUNDS
1 dangerous, enjoyable, intelligent, judge, journalist, language, manager, soldier, surgeon
2 /tʃ/ chance coach rich teacher
/ʃ/: efficient fashionable professional patient receptionist Russian sociable

READING
2 2
3 ...must be just as lazy...
...they must be trying to hide something.   ...they might just be out running...   He could be a guitar-playing...   ...he might be just posing as one.   ...he might be an ageing hippie.   He must be one if...   He could be a company executive...   he must come from a conservative background...
4 3

GRAMMAR
1 2 He can't have a job.   3 They must be tourists.   4 She must be a sports reporter.   5 He can't be a doctor.   6 She can't be stupid.
2 2 She could be a teacher, but she might also be a nurse.
3 She could be a shop assistant, but she might also be the manager.   4 He could be a guide, but he might also be a coach driver.

Lesson 19

VOCABULARY

2 1 package 2 guided tour
3 remote places 4 backpack
5 charter flight 6 first class
7 souvenirs

FUNCTIONS

1 1 ✖ 2 ✖ 3 ✔ 4 ✔ 5 ✖
2 *Example answers* 2 You have
to fasten your seat belt during
landing. You are not allowed to
smoke during take off.
3 You are not supposed to take
photos of paintings. You are not
allowed to touch the paintings.
4 You are not supposed to lean
out of the windows. You have
to show your ticket.

READING

1 a traveller's guide to
photography
2 1 keep to them 2 no 3 take it
away 4 far from the big
centres 5 disapprove 6 in the
country
3 not allowed to photograph:
military installations, women in
Islamic countries, interiors of
mosques obliged to do: obtain
a photographic permit, show it
to frontier officials, pay people
to pose allowed to
photograph:exteriors of
mosques, ancient Chinese
monuments, religious temples in
China not supposed to
photograph: some industrial
plants, some trains, some
bridges

Lesson 20

VOCABULARY

1 bad-mannered, cool-headed,
easygoing, fair-minded, good-
tempered, hard-working,
middle-aged, old-fashioned,
right-handed, self-assured,
short-sighted, soft-hearted,
world-famous, well-behaved
2 1 bad-mannered 2 cool-
headed 3 hard-working
4 old-fashioned
5 world-famous

GRAMMAR

1 1 was able to 2 could 3 was
able to 4 could 5 could
2 general ability: 2, 4, 5
specific occasion: 1, 3
4 1 couldn't *or* wasn't able to
2 be able to 3 couldn't 4 can
or are able to 5 can *or* could
6 have been able to
7 can 8 wasn't able to
5 3, 4, 7, 8

Lesson 21

VOCABULARY

1 horizontal: boring, safe,
remarkable, bad, dense, loud,
old, funny, awkward,
delightful vertical: brilliant,
exciting, unusual, fast, live,
slow, good, dull, sudden, entire

2 1 loudly 2 badly 3 fast
4 entirely 5 brilliantly
6 safely 7 suddenly 8 well

GRAMMAR

1 absolutely, awfully, beautifully,
emotionally, exceptionally,
extremely, fantastically,
outstandingly, particularly,
simply, really, terribly
2 *Example answers*
2 particularly 3 simply
4 really 5 terribly 6 awfully

LISTENING

1 The woman has seen it, the
man hasn't. It is a comedy.
2 Read the tapescript and check
your answers.

SOUNDS

1 absolutely, amazingly,
especially, extraordinarily,
extremely, incredibly,
particularly, really, remarkably,
terribly
2 1 extremely film 2 acting
really brilliant 3 special effects
absolutely extraordinary
4 opening scene terribly funny
5 plot remarkably 6 ending
completely

READING

1 3
2 1 *The Birds* 2 Alfred Hitchcock
3 A thriller
(or perhaps a horror film)
4 Tippi Hedren and Rod Taylor
3 extremely (good-looking),
discreetly (leaves), violently
(attacks), increasingly (vicious),
frantically (fight), finally
(manage to escape)

Lesson 22

VOCABULARY

Across: 1 whale, 5 eagle, 7 bear,
8 poach, 10 fly, 11 cat,
12 fox
Down: 1 wild, 2 lion, 3 tiger,
4 species, 5 elephant, 6 ivory,
9 wolf

GRAMMAR

1 manner: slowly, by car,
suddenly, sharply, on foot,
gradually, officially,
place: in the wild, all over the
country, in Asia, in the
mountains, there, everywhere,
in the west
time: last year, soon, in 1965, at
first, then, finally, ten years ago
2 2 this year (time) 3 suddenly
(manner); last week (time)
4 in the mountains (place); on
foot (manner) 5 In the 1960s
(time) 6 In Europe (place);
today (time)
3 1 Thousands of years ago
humans killed animals for food
and clothing. Humans killed
animals for food and clothing
thousands of years ago.
2 Many species have completely
disappeared. Many species have
disappeared completely.
3 Today there are laws that

protect some animals. There are
laws today that protect some
animals. 4 But many poachers
still shoot animals illegally.
5 In some places people have
reintroduced animals. People
have reintroduced animals in
some places. 6 For instance,
naturalists have reintroduced
lynx in Switzerland.

READING

1 A: kiwi B: bald eagle
Correct statements = 1, 3, 5.
2 gradually, sadly, this year,
rapidly, from the forests, for
thousands of years, ten years
ago, today, immediately,
completely, in less than ten
years, rapidly, until modern
times, in the past, in the vast
forests, thousands of years ago,
in New Zealand, extremely
3 1 b 2 d 3 c 4 e 5 a
4 A: gradually B: majestically

Lesson 23

VOCABULARY

2 happy – content, faithful – true,
jealous – suspicious,
honest – truthful, selfish –
mean, cruel – unkind,
passionate – intense, sad –
unhappy
3 faithfulness, jealousy, honesty,
selfishness, cruelty, passion,
sadness

GRAMMAR

1 2 He said he had sent her a
Valentine card. 3 He said he
loved her. 4 He said he was
the happiest man in the world.
5 He said he had bought her a
diamond ring. 6 He said he
was getting married on
Saturday.
2 2 She said they would see them
the next day. 3 She said she
had come back from London
three weeks before.
4 They said they had got home
late the night before. 5 She
said she was staying at home
that day. 6 He said he was not
going out that night.

SOUNDS

1 /ʃ/ passionate selfish suspicious
shrink reflection sure
/s/ selfish suspicious satin kiss
scent possessive fierce
/z/ rose possessive always
doesn't
2 1 truth loop 2 tears fierce
3 heart card 4 ring lips
5 blind Valentine 6 grief feel

READING

1 1 and 3 are true.
2 1 She said she was cold.
2 He said that his love would
keep her warm. 3 She said she
was still cold. 4 He said she
could have some money.
5 He said she could buy herself
a fur coat.

3 *Example answers*
1 weak resigned 2 cynical
3 ironic

Lesson 24

VOCABULARY

1 *Example answers* Television:
serial, screen, remote control,
viewers, episode, programme,
show, series, channel, media,
audience. The other words
could be used to talk about
newspapers.
2 1 programmes 2 screen
3 remote control 4 tabloid
5 media

READING

1 1 D 2 B 3 C 4 A
2 1 a lot 2 a lot 3 the whole
serial carefully 4 a lot of free
time 5 a lot
4 1 It is an instrument of culture
only to a very limited extent.
2 Egyptians watch more
television, especially serials,
than people in most other
countries. 3 The majority are
American. 4 They attract all
age groups. 5 Besides the
normal shows, special serials
are run during Ramadan.

LISTENING

1 documentary sports soap
opera the news film
2 1 h 2 c 3 a 4 f 5 e 6 b 7
g 8 d

GRAMMAR

1 2 She asked what he was doing
that evening. 3 She asked if
they had shown the finals of the
men's tennis.
4 He asked what channel it was
on. 5 He asked what the
second episode had been like.
6 She asked who had won.
7 She asked if he wanted her to
record the documentary for him.
8 He asked if she had watched
the sport the previous night.
2 2 'Are you going to the cinema?'
she asked. 3 'Are you
interested in sport?' he asked.
4 'Why don't you watch the
soap?' she asked.
5 'Do you prefer the news on
the radio or the television?' he
asked. 6 'Can you record a
movie?' she asked.

Lesson 25

GRAMMAR

1 1 c 2 d 3 a 4 e 5 b
2 *Example answers*
1 'I'll take you to the park.'
2 'Would you like to take over
the sales department?'
3 'We'll be late.' 4 'We were
late because of the traffic.'
5 'No, thank you.'

READING

1 1 c 2 a 3 f 4 d 5 e 6 b
2 a one of the men e Mr Wallis
f them
b: 1 c: 1 d: 3 e: 2 f: 4

3 1 Mr Langley asked the doctor why Mr Wallis had died.
2 The doctor admitted that he didn't know. 3 Mr Langley reminded the doctor that Mr Wallis had been fine before he moved into the room.
4 He warned the doctor that there was something wrong with the bed. 5 The doctor tried to persuade Mr Langley to move into the spare room.
6 Mr Langley refused to move into the spare room.
4 1 He refused to move into the room. 2 He said he'd rather sleep in the toilet. 3 The night sister asked if the doctor could go and see Mr Howell.
4 She said he was fine, but a little upset.

WRITING
1 I was off that weekend. When I came back the side room was empty. The story was that he had died in his sleep in the bed that everyone now associated with death. The post-mortem found no obvious explanation.

Lesson 26
READING
1 Rattlesnake meat; America
3 alligator, kangaroo, ostrich
VOCABULARY
1 Horizontal: spread, fry, peel, chop, mix, heat, slice, serve, taste
Vertical: bake, boil, pour, cut, roast, grill, put, oil, add, cool, soak
2 *Example answers*
1 Put/Soak 2 Cool
3 Slice/Chop 4 Add
5 Spread 6 Put 7 Pour
8 Chop 9 Add 10 Fry/Heat
LISTENING
2 2 a cake 1 hamburgers
3 a mixed salad
3 Speaker 1: c, f, j
Speaker 2: b, e, h, k
Speaker 3: a, d, g, i
GRAMMAR
1 2 Always dry the lettuce well.
3 Never boil the chocolate.
4 Never use olive oil with walnuts. 5 Always add lemon juice to avocados.
2 2 Don't forget to oil the baking tin. 3 Make sure you put the oven on to heat. 4 Don't forget to add a spoonful of flour. 5 Make sure the mixture is creamy.

Lesson 27
VOCABULARY
1 1 which 2 who 3 where
4 which 5 which 6 where
7 who 8 which
2 1 ferry 2 guest 3 built-up area 4 wreck 5 visa
6 hotel 7 interior designer
8 island

GRAMMAR
1 1 which/that 2 where
3 where 4 who 5 whose
6 which/that 7 which/that
8 whose
2 Sentences 1, 4, 6 and 7.
3 2 Was the museum you visited this morning interesting?
3 Was the map you bought at the station very useful?
4 There weren't many people on the beach you told us about.
5 Have you met the couple sitting by the window?
6 I showed her the photos I took of Paris. 7 Did you find the restaurant I recommended.
8 Have you ever been back to the Greek island where you met your husband?
SOUNDS
1 that 2 – 3 which 4 –
5 which 6 that
READING
1 No, they didn't enjoy their holidays.
2 A: disappointing
B: frightening
3 A: ...some Americans who we had met... ...didn't know the people who we were staying with... ...most disappointing holiday that I've had...
B: ...and the screams that we had heard... ...the most frightening experience that I've ever had.
LISTENING
a Speaker 1 b Speaker 3
c Speaker 2 d Speaker 4
e Speaker 2 f Speaker 4
g Speaker 3

Lesson 28
VOCABULARY
1 reduction – reduce, building – build, discovery – discover production – produce, growth – grow, design – design increase – increase, invention – invent, distribution – distribute
2 bread – wheat, plastic – petrol, whisky – barley, cheese – milk, steel – iron-ore, paper – wood, wine – grapes, cider – apples, china – kaolin
3 *Example answers*
distillery – alcohol, vineyard – grapes/wine, factory – manufactured goods, power station – electricity, pottery – china/dishes, mine – coal/gold
GRAMMAR
1 2 Whisky is distilled in Scotland. 3 Gold is mined in South Africa. 4 Beer is brewed in Denmark. 5 Cars are built in Germany.
6 Electronic goods are manufactured in Japan.
2 2 Vegetables are grown in Brittany. 3 Wine is produced in Bordeaux and Burgundy.
4 Perfume is made in the south east. 5 Planes are

manufactured in the south west of France. 6 Coal is mined in the north east of France.
7 Clothes are designed in Paris.
3 2 are manufactured 3 is thought; was first discovered
4 has been reduced 5 have been built 6 have been produced 7 will be imported
8 will be processed and distributed
4 2 Whisky is exported all over the world. 3 The coal mining industry is being affected by nuclear power. 4 Pottery was first made here in the 18th century. 5 The glass industry was being developed over 100 years ago. 6 The production of steel will be increased.
WRITING
1 cheese: milk paper: trees, wood pulp bread: yeast, wheat, oven plastic: refined, oil, chemical process
wine: ferment, grapes, vineyard, bottle, water
2 *Example answers*
The cows are milked every day. The milk is stored in a tank. A lorry collects the milk.
It is taken to the dairy. The milk is warmed. It is left to ferment for 24 hours. The yoghurt is put into individual pots.
It is delivered to the shop.

Lesson 29
VOCABULARY
1 1 my husband 2 an electrician
3 a decorator
4 a plumber 5 a gardener
6 a builder 7 a carpenter
8 a mechanic
2 *Example answers*
2 The flower beds are full of weeds. 3 The lawn is overgrown. 4 The window panes are broken. 5 Slates are missing from the roof. 6 The paint is peeling.
LISTENING
1 Read the tapescript and check your answers.
2 Speaker 1 is the most self-sufficient. Speaker 3 is the least self-sufficient.
GRAMMAR
3 2 The tyre needs changing. I'll get the mechanic to change it.
3 The car needs cleaning. I'll get my father to clean it.
4 The battery needs checking. I'll get a friend to check it.
5 The car needs repairing. I'll get a mechanic to repair it.
6 The headlights need changing. I'll get someone to change them.
4 2 The tyre needs to be changed. 3 The car needs to be cleaned. 4 The battery needs to be checked. 5 The car needs to be repaired.
6 The headlights need to be changed.

Lesson 30
VOCABULARY
2 dangerous, easy, essential, expensive, important, necessary, polite, right, sensible, stupid, unpleasant, wrong
3 *Example answers*
1 dangerous 2 important
3 essential 4 sensible
5 expensive 6 necessary
7 stupid 8 polite
SOUNDS
1 goal 2 foot 3 fast 4 wooden
GRAMMAR
1 1 make 2 don't let 3 make
4 don't let 5 let 6 don't let
2 2 They don't let you go hang gliding until you are sixteen.
3 They make you show a medical certificate to take diving lessons.
4 They don't let children go climbing without an adult.
5 They don't let skiers practise on the track before a race.
6 They make you have a licence to own a gun.
7 They let children go on the golf course if they don't make a noise.
READING AND WRITING
1 1 B 2 A 3 C
2 *Example answers*
1 The competitors were driving too fast. The route was not safe.
2 Heavy rain had turned the river into a raging torrent. The participants were inexperienced. 3 It was getting dark at the time. He was shooting very near home.

Lesson 31
GRAMMAR
2 2 I always take my umbrella in case it rains.
3 I have a big breakfast in case I don't have time for lunch.
4 I always take a petrol-can in case I run out of petrol.
5 I always check my agenda in case I forget an important appointment.
3 1 in case 2 if 3 in case
4 if 5 if 6 if
VOCABULARY
2 Across: 1 umbrella 9 coffee
14 towel 15 string 16 plug
Down: 2 lamp 4 binoculars
5 knife 7 diary 10 soap
11 flag
Across:
8 I always take some with me in case the banks are shut.
12 I always buy one if I visit a town I don't know.
Down:
3 If you have one of these, you can see where you're going in the dark.
6 You can read this if you have a long wait between planes.
13 I always have one in my bag in case I want to write something down.

LISTENING
2 1 He 2 He 3 She 4 He
5 She 6 He 7 She 8 She
9 He 10 He
3 a 10 b 7 c 3 d 5 e 1 f 4
g 8 h 9 i 2 j 6

Lesson 32
VOCABULARY
1 e 2 c 3 d 4 i 5 h 6 a
7 g 8 b 9 f
LISTENING
2 Conversation 1: a – television
Yes Conversation 2: f –
kitchen cupboard kit Yes
Conversation 3: e – radio No
Conversation 4: g – washing
machine Yes
3 1 I'll send; he has finished
2 I'll explain; he comes in
3 I'll be; you have found
4 I'll send; it gets in
GRAMMAR
1 1 He'll come; I have finished
2 we'll send 3 I'll phone
4 I have seen 5 I'll make
6 you bring; we'll check
2 1 likely to 2 likely to
3 expected to 4 due to
5 likely to 6 due to
READING AND WRITING
1 1 e 2 c 3 i 4 j 5 a
6 d 7 h 8 f 9 b 10 g

Lesson 33
GRAMMAR
1 2 Drink strong coffee to stay
awake on a long journey.
3 Leave dirty silver to soak in
Coca Cola to remove stains.
4 Clean your windows with wet
newspaper to make them really
shine.
5 Leave a candle burning to get
rid of the smell of cigarette
smoke.
6 Pour a little vinegar in the
water to stop peeled potatoes
going black.
2 1 d 2 a 3 e 4 b 5 c
3 2 To remove wine from the
carpet, put salt on it
immediately.
3 To get rid of hiccups, ask a
friend to frighten you.
4 To clean your teeth, brush
them occasionally with salt.
5 To polish your windscreen,
rub it with an onion.
VOCABULARY
1 top row: toothpaste, a tie, a
windscreen; next row: some
tomatoes, an ice cube, a
cabbage; next row: some
matches, some shoes, a fridge;
bottom row: a hairdryer, an
ashtray, a fly
READING
1 a Association b Substitution
c Classification d Rhymes
2 to spell the word 'piece';
to recall the shape of Italy;
to remember abstract
information; to help them
remember things; To spell the
words 'receive' and 'believe';

To remember which takes 'ie'
and which takes 'ei'.
3 1 If you train yourself in a
number of simple techniques,
you can improve your memory.
2 To remember new
information, use the technique
of association.
3 To remember names,
associate them with a visual
image. 4 If you want to
remember something abstract,
think of anything that reminds
you of the word. 5 You can
remember lists of words or
objects by classifying them.
6 You can train yourself to
associate things by asking a
number of questions.

Lesson 34
SOUNDS
1 1 economy economic ✔
2 appreciate appreciation ✔
3 consume consumption
4 energy energetic ✔
5 environment environmental ✔
6 hospitable hospitality ✔
7 accommodate
accommodation ✔
2 /g/ give guide guest language
/dʒ/ damage energy language
suggestion
silent 'g' foreign sights
READING
2 1 If you reduce your petrol
consumption, you will save
money. 2 Avoid buying plastic
bottles, they pollute the oceans.
3 If everyone uses less
electricity, there will be less
nuclear waste. 4 If you take a
shower instead of a bath, you
will save water.
5 If you buy a microwave oven,
you will use less energy.
3 2
4 2 you will need to be very
independent and self-sufficient
3 you'll need to think about
everything very carefully
4 make sure you choose your
companion carefully 5 you
will probably be the focus of
interest 6 locals will appreciate
it 7 do write to them 8 you
will need specialised equipment
9 you will discover exciting
places which on your own you
would probably miss 10 you
won't have to carry a heavy
backpack.
GRAMMAR
1 1 If you go to Greece, you will
have good weather. 2 If you
travel out of season, you will
avoid crowds. 3 If you don't
take a guide book, you will get
lost. 4 If you don't like the
heat, you won't like Morocco.
5 If you appreciate spicy food,
you will enjoy India.
2 2 will discover; hire 3 stay;
will cost 4 won't spend; travel
5 have; will enjoy
6 like; will enjoy

Lesson 35
READING
1 He is a truck driver.
Because every night for a year
he has dreamed that he was
knocked down by a truck.
2 3
3 1 after Frank shot up from his
pillow, frightened. 2 after He
was himself a truck driver,...
3 after She felt sure that the
dreams would stop if he did.
4 after And this morning he had
a surprise for her.
5 after Frank was on one of his
regular journeys.
GRAMMAR
1 1 past perfect continuous
2 past perfect simple
2 1 She had been a truck driver;
when 2 she had flown round
the world; when/after 3 she
had made; after/when 4 she
had broken the record
After/When 5 worked there;
because 6 she had been
7 truck driving had exhausted
him; because
3 2 She said he had tried to stop
the truck in time. 3 He said he
had enjoyed his job before the
dreams had started. 4 She said
she hadn't seen the
documentary about Amelia
Earhart. 5 He said she had
worked hard until she retired.
4 1 Things had been going well
for him
2 that had been terrifying him
5 2 He had been trying to avoid
the pedestrian when the truck
hit the glass tower. 3 She had
been flying over the Pacific
Ocean when the plane
crashed. 4 He had been having
the same dream until he
died. 5 He had been living
comfortably until he lost his
job. 6 She had been flying for
twenty years when she
disappeared.
VOCABULARY
1 Amelia Earhart: capture, crash,
disappear, drown, equator,
exhausted, feminism, fuel,
mystery, propaganda, record,
retire, rumour, solo, strained,
survive, true Truck driver:
brakes, concentration, control,
crash, delivery, died, dream,
gardener, glass, huge, hurtling,
mask, pavement, pedestrian,
pieces, pillow, reflection,
screamed, terror, tower

Lesson 36
SOUNDS
1 friendly 2 warning 3 friendly
4 friendly 5 friendly 6 warning
GRAMMAR
1 1 told 2 knew 3 wouldn't
settle down 4 found out
5 went out 6 married
READING
2 a 4 b 7 c 1 d 5 e 2 f 8 g
3 h 6

LISTENING
1 Conversation 1: 2
Conversation 2: 6
Conversation 3: 3
2 Read the tapescript and check
your answers.

Lesson 37
GRAMMAR
1 2 She oughtn't to have worn
flip-flops in the restaurant.
3 He oughtn't to have eaten so
much dinner. 4 You ought to
have told me where you were
going. 5 They ought to have
checked the price of the room
first. 6 We oughtn't to have
bought so many cigarettes.
2 1 He shouldn't have insisted on
paying. 2 She shouldn't have
filmed people at prayer.
She should have taken off her
shoes. 3 She shouldn't have
eaten her hamburger in the
street. She shouldn't have
blown her nose in public.
SOUNDS
2 1 good 2 humid 3 wait 4 wear
LISTENING
1 Conversation 1: Picture B, yes
Conversation 2: Picture C, yes
Conversation 3: Picture A, no
2 beautiful authentic elegant
busy sweet pleasant
4 She should have taken warm
clothes and snow boots. She
should have stayed in a hotel
closer to the centre. She should
have booked through a travel
agent.
5 She ought to have taken more
traveller's cheques. She ought to
have noted down the numbers
of the cheques. She ought to
have bought bottled water. She
ought to have used sun tan
cream. She shouldn't have put
her luggage down on the
bench. She shouldn't have
taken so much cash with her.
She shouldn't have spent all day
on the beach. She shouldn't
have drunk from the fountain.

Lesson 38
GRAMMAR
1 1 ✘ 2 ✔ 3 ✘ 4 ✘ 5 ✔
READING
1 He is in a haunted house.
He made a bet with friends.
2 1 b 2 d 3 a 4 c 5 e 6 f
3 1 darker 2 because it was wet
3 a sudden idea 4 it had
disappeared 5 wiped his
forehead
4 They give the impression that
there are two people: the
footsteps continue when he has
stopped walking, his watch is
on the wrong wrist and he pulls
his handkerchief out of the
wrong pocket; the word figure
suggests that it may not be the
same person who leaves the
house.

SOUNDS

heart – glance, mopped – gone
turn – learn, find – tiles, wrist –
miss, reach – beat, clue – through,
won – come

VOCABULARY

1 heart 2 beat 3 wrist 4 glance

Lesson 39

GRAMMAR

1 2 We lost the match.
  3 I studied computer
  programming. 4 I left him
  alone. 5 Your mother won't let
  you come to the festival.
  6 We have to leave before the
  end. 7 I didn't work hard at
  school. 8 You didn't warn me
  before I left.

2 2 I wish I had gone to
  university. 3 I wish I had
  known my grandparents.
  4 I wish I was a better cook.
  5 I wish I hadn't lost touch with
  my cousins. 6 I wish I had a
  more interesting job.

3 2 If only I had gone to
  university. 3 If only I had
  known my grandparents.
  4 If only I was a better cook.
  5 If only I hadn't lost touch with
  my cousins.
  6 If only I had a more
  interesting job.

LISTENING

1 Speaker 1: an old-fashioned
  prep school He liked it.
  Speaker 2: a village primary
  school She didn't like it.
  Speaker 3: a public school He
  liked it.

2 a 3 b 1 c 3 d 3 e 2 f 2 g
  1 h 1 i 2 j 3

3 2 I wish I hadn't given up
  languages. 3 I wish I hadn't
  spent such a lot of time doing
  homework. 4 I wish I hadn't
  chosen Latin. 5 I wish I had
  been happy at school.
  6 I wish I had enjoyed myself
  more. 7 I wish I had worked
  harder at school. 8 I wish I
  hadn't failed my exams.
  9 I wish I had gone to a
  boarding school. 10 I wish I
  had done Spanish.

READING

1 unhappy

2 1 intelligent 2 unkind 3 not
  4 hold it close to you
  5 unpleasant 6 isolate him/her
  7 stupid

3 1 I'm seven 2 I'm dead bright
  3 Sometimes trying to
  understand them makes me cry.
  Words They make me sick
  inside. 4 Sometimes trying to
  understand them makes me cry.
  Words hurt Words are all over
  the place. They get shoved in
  my face. 5 I can't even ask for
  help Lock me away from what I
  want to say. 6 Words are
  bullies. Words are mean.

7 Sneaky things. They gabble and
  lie. Words spread nasty gossip
4 He would agree with 1 and 3.
5 I wish words were things you
  could hug. I wish they came in
  bottles.
  Example answers I wish words
  didn't gabble and lie. I wish I
  could understand what people
  say. I wish I could ask for help.
  I wish I could express myself. I
  wish people wouldn't think I'm
  thick.

Lesson 40

VOCABULARY

1 They are all verbs. These words
  are also nouns: curse,
  encounter, flicker, frown, gleam,
  laugh, murder, picnic, whistle.

2 1 encounter 2 whistling
  3 threatened 4 picnic 5 was
  following 6 murder 7 laugh

SOUNDS

1 building, laugh, neighbourhood,
  whistle, though, frighten,
  grandmother, night, sign, would

2 1 stride 2 frown 3 journey
  4 sure

3 /e/ threaten breath dead
  /ɜ:/ heard
  /i:/ beat breathing leave reading
  gleam
  /eɪ/ break

GRAMMAR

1 1 d 2 e 3 a 4 b 5 c

2 2 I would have walked home if
  I had missed the bus.
  3 Helen would have got very
  wet if she had forgotten her
  umbrella.
  4 Chloé would have been very
  upset if you had not come to
  see her.
  5 Dieter would have joined the
  local football club earlier if he
  had heard about it.
  6 Felix would have missed the
  flight if he had gone to the
  meeting.

READING

1 1 C 2 D 3 A 4 B

2 *Example answers*
  If the robber hadn't given the
  cashier a note with his name
  and address written on it, he
  might not have been caught.
  If the man hadn't carried sand in
  his suitcase, the customs officials
  would have looked more closely
  at his bicycle.
  If the forger hadn't printed his
  own portrait on the notes he
  might not have been caught.
  If they hadn't thrown the tickets
  away they would have won the
  prize.

3 1 the robber 2 yes 3 illegal
  4 someone who makes false
  money 5 unhappy 6 a place
  where rubbish is put

Wordlist

The first number after each word
shows the lesson in which the
word first appears in the
vocabulary box. The numbers in
italics show the later lessons in
which the word appears again.

able /ˈeɪb(ə)l/ PC 11-15
accelerator /əkˈseləˌreɪtə(r)/ 32
accommodation /əˌkɒməˈdeɪʃ(ə)n/ 37
accustomed /əˈkʌstəmd/ PC 11-15
acquaintance /əˈkweɪnt(ə)ns/ 36
action film /ˈækʃ(ə)n fɪlm/ 21
activity /ækˈtɪvɪti/ 1
address /əˈdres/ 1
address book /əˈdres bʊk/ 31
adore /əˈdɔː(r)/ 25
advertisement /ədˈvɜːtɪsmənt/ 24
aerial /ˈeərɪəl/ 32
afford /əˈfɔːd/ 8
afraid /əˈfreɪd/ PC 11-15
aggressive /əˈgresɪv/ 20, 23
air force /ˈeə(r) fɔːs/ 12
alarm clock /əˈlɑːm klɒk/ 15, 31
alive /əˈlaɪv/ PC 11-15
all right /ˈɔːl raɪt/ 4
allergic /əˈlɜːdʒɪk/ PC 11-15
alone /əˈləʊn/ PC 11-15
aloud /əˈlaʊd/ 1
amazing /əˈmeɪzɪŋ/ 21
ambition /æmˈbɪʃ(ə)n/ 6
amusing /əˈmjuːzɪŋ/ 5
angry /ˈæŋgri/ PC 11-15, 23
announcement /əˈnaʊnsmənt/ 2
answer /ˈɑːnsə(r)/ 1
antique /ænˈtiːk/ 15
antique shop /ænˈtiːk ʃɒp/ 25
apart /əˈpɑːt/ PC 11-15
appalling /əˈpɔːlɪŋ/ 21
appear /əˈpɪə(r)/ 13
apple /ˈæp(ə)l/ 23
appreciate /əˈpriːʃɪeɪt/ 34
armchair /ˈɑːmtʃeə(r)/ 15, 29
army /ˈɑːmi/ 12
aroma /əˈrəʊmə/ 33
arrival /əˈraɪv(ə)l/ 2
art gallery /ˈɑːt gæləri/ 14
art /ˈɑːt/ 39
article /ˈɑːtɪk(ə)l/ 24
ash /æʃ/ 33
ashtray /ˈæʃtreɪ/ 15
ask /ɑːsk/ 1
ask somebody out
  /ɑːsk ˈsʌmbədi aʊt/ 36
assertive /əˈsɜːtɪv/ 20
assume /əˈsjuːm/ 38
astonished /əˈstɒnɪʃt/ PC 6-10
athlete /ˈæθliːt/ 30
athletics /æθˈletɪks/ 30
attack /əˈtæk/ 12
autumn /ˈɔːtəm/ 37
avocado /ˌævəˈkɑːdəʊ/ 26
avoid /əˈvɔɪd/ 34
awful /ˈɔːfl/ 4
awkward /ˈɔːkwəd/ 21

backpack /ˈbækpæk/ 19
baggage /ˈbægɪdʒ/ 2
bags /bægz/ 7
bake /beɪk/ 26
ballpoint pen /ˈbɔːlpɔɪnt pen/ 31
bamboo basket /bæmˈbuː bɑːskɪt/ 37
banana /bəˈnɑːnə/ 8
bananas /bəˈnɑːnəz/ 28
bandage /ˈbændɪdʒ/ 28
bank worker /ˈbæŋk ˌwɜːkə(r)/ 18
bar /bɑː(r)/ 9
baseball /ˈbeɪsbɔːl/ 13
baseball cap /ˈbeɪsbɔːl kæp/ 16
basket /ˈbɑːskɪt/ 30, 33

basketball /ˈbɑːskɪtbɔːl/ 30
bath /bɑːθ/ 29
battle /ˈbæt(ə)l/ 12
be born /bi bɔːn/ 1
beach /biːtʃ/ 27
bean /biːn/ 9
beans /biːnz/ 26
bear (n) /beə(r)/ 22
beard /bɪəd/ 16
beat /biːt/ 40
beautiful /ˈbjuːtɪfl/ 17
beer /bɪə(r)/ 28
beetroot /ˈbiːtruːt/ 8
beige /beɪʒ/ 16
bell /bel/ 25
belt /belt/ 16
best man /best mæn/ 3
bias /ˈbaɪəs/ 24
bicycle /ˈbaɪsɪkl/ 15, 19
bikini /bɪˈkiːni/ 16, 37
binoculars /bɪˈnɒkjʊləz/ 31
bird-watching /ˈbɜːdwɒtʃɪŋ/ 4
birthday /ˈbɜːθdeɪ/ 1
bitter /ˈbɪtə(r)/ 8, 9
blanket /ˈblæŋkɪt/ 33
blocked /blɒkt/ 29
blow up /ˈbləʊ ʌp/ PC 21-25
blues /bluːz/ 5
boarding school /ˈbɔːdɪŋ skuːl/ 39
boil /bɔɪl/ 26
boiling water /ˈbɔɪlɪŋ ˈwɔːtə(r)/ 33
bomb /bɒm/ 12
bonnet /ˈbɒnɪt/ 32
booking office /ˈbʊkɪŋ ɒfɪs/ 2
boot /buːt/ 25, 32
boots /buːts/ 30
border /ˈbɔːdə(r)/ 12
bored /bɔːd/ PC 11-15
boring /ˈbɔːrɪŋ/ 4, 5
bow tie /bəʊ taɪ/ 16
bowl /bəʊl/ 26
box /bɒks/ 25
boxer /ˈbɒksə(r)/ 30
boxer shorts /ˈbɒksə(r) ʃɔːts/ 16
boxing /ˈbɒksɪŋ/ 30
boyfriend /ˈbɔɪfrend/ 36
brake /breɪk/ 32
brake light /breɪk laɪt/ 32
bread /bred/ 8
break up /breɪk ʌp/ 36
bride /braɪd/ 3
bridesmaid /ˈbraɪdzmeɪd/ 3
bridge /brɪdʒ/ 14
bright /braɪt/ 33
brilliant /ˈbrɪliənt/ 4
broadcast /ˈbrɔːdkɑːst/ 24
broadsheet /ˈbrɔːdʃiːt/ 24
broken /ˈbrəʊkən/ 29
brother /ˈbrʌðə(r)/ 1
brush /brʌʃ/ 17
brush off /brʌʃ ɒf/ 33
build /bɪld/ 28
builder /ˈbɪldə(r)/ 29
bullet /ˈbʊlɪt/ 12
bumper /ˈbʌmpə(r)/ 32
bunch /bʌntʃ/ 10
burst /bɜːst/ 2
business card /ˈbɪznɪs kɑːd/ 31
busy /ˈbɪzi/ 11, 14
butter /ˈbʌtə(r)/ 9
butterfly /ˈbʌtəflaɪ/ 22
buy /baɪ/ 7, 11

cab /kæb/ 2
cab rank /kæb ræŋk/ 2
cabbage /ˈkæbɪdʒ/ 8
cake /keɪk/ 3
canal /kəˈnæl/ 27
canary /kəˈneəri/ 16
cancel /ˈkæns(ə)l/ 2
canvas /ˈkænvəs/ 16
capable /ˈkeɪpəb(ə)l/ PC 11-15
capture /ˈkæptʃə(r)/ 35
car horn /kɑː hɔːn/ 2
car repair /kɑː rɪˈpeə(r)/ 39

cardigan /ˈkɑːdɪgən/ 16
carpenter /ˈkɑːpɪntə(r)/ 29
carpet /ˈkɑːpɪt/ 29, 33
carry /ˈkærɪ/ 7
cars /kɑːz/ 28
cartoon /kɑːˈtuːn/ 13
cash /kæʃ/ 3, 31
casserole /ˈkæsərəʊl/ 26
cassette player /kəˈset ˈpleɪə(r)/ 32
castle /ˈkɑːs(ə)l/ 14
casual /ˈkæʒʊəl/ 10
casually /ˈkæʒʊəlɪ/ 40
catch /kætʃ/ 2
catch up with
   /ˈkætʃ ʌp wɪθ/ PC 21-25
cathedral /kəˈθiːdrəl/ 14, 19
cause /kɔːz/ 34
ceiling /ˈsiːlɪŋ/ 29
cemetery /ˈsemətrɪ/ 14
ceremony /ˈserɪmənɪ/ 3
certain /ˈsɜːt(ə)n/ PC 11-15
channel /ˈtʃæn(ə)l/ 24
charming /ˈtʃɑːmɪŋ/ 21
chart /tʃɑːt/ 1
chat show /ˈtʃæt ʃəʊ/ 24
chatter /ˈtʃætə(r)/ 38
check /tʃek/ 1
chemical /ˈkemɪk(ə)l/ 9
chemistry /ˈkemɪstrɪ/ 39
cheque book /ˈtʃek bʊk/ 31
chewing gum /ˈtʃuːɪŋ gʌm/ 33
children /ˈtʃɪldrən/ 1
chilly /ˈtʃɪlɪ/ 8
china /ˈtʃaɪnə/ 15, 28
chocolate /ˈtʃɒklət/ 16, 31
chop /tʃɒp/ 26
Christian /ˈkrɪstɪən/ 3
chrysanthemum /krɪˈsænθəməm/ 23
church /tʃɜːtʃ/ 3, 19
circle /ˈsɜːk(ə)l/ 1
circulation /ˌsɜːkjʊˈleɪʃ(ə)n/ 24
classical /ˈklæsɪk(ə)l/ 5
clean /kliːn/ 11, 29
clock /klɒk/ 33
cloth /klɒθ/ 28
club /klʌb/ 12
clue /kluː/ 38
clumsy /ˈklʌmzɪ/ 21
clutch /klʌtʃ/ 32
coach /kəʊtʃ/ 2
coal /kəʊl/ 28, 33
coast-to-coast /kəʊst tə kəʊst/ 35
cocoa /ˈkəʊkəʊ/ 9
coffee /ˈkɒfɪ/ 28
coffee cup /ˈkɒfɪ kʌp/ 15
coffee-house /ˈkɒfɪ haʊs/ 14
cold /kəʊld/ 9
colleague /ˈkɒliːg/ 10
collect /kəˈlekt/ 11
comedy /ˈkɒmədɪ/ 21
comic /ˈkɒmɪk/ 13
commercial /kəˈmɜːʃ(ə)l/ 24
companion /kəmˈpænɪən/ 38
compete /kəmˈpiːt/ 30
complain about /kəmˈpleɪn əˈbaʊt/ 7
complete /kəmˈpliːt/ 1
comprehensive school
   /ˌkɒmprɪˈhensɪv skuːl/ 39
computer studies
   /kəmˈpjuːtə(r) ˈstʌdɪz/ 39
computers /kəmˈpjuːtəz/ 28
concert hall /ˈkɒnsət hɔːl/ 14
confidence /ˈkɒnfɪdəns/ 6
confident /ˈkɒnfɪdənt/ PC 11-15, 20
confused /kənˈfjuːzd/ 8
connection /kəˈnekʃn/ 1
consumption /kənˈsʌmʃ(ə)n/ 34
conversation /ˌkɒnvəˈseɪʃn/ 1
cook /kʊk/ 26
cool /kuːl/ 40
cool-headed /ˈkuːl hedɪd/ 20
cosmopolitan /ˌkɒzməˈpɒlɪt(ə)n/ 14
cost /kɒst/ 7
cotton /ˈkɒtn/ 15, 16, 28

country and western
   /ˈkʌntrɪ ənd ˈwest(ə)n/ 5
couple /ˈkʌp(ə)l/ 3
court /kɔːt/ 30
cover /ˈkʌvə(r)/ 38
crash /kræʃ/ 35
crazy /ˈkreɪzɪ/ 40
cream /kriːm/ 16, 26
credit card /ˈkredɪt kɑːd/ 31
crew cut /ˈkruː kʌt/ 16
cricket /ˈkrɪkɪt/ 4
criminal /ˈkrɪmɪn(ə)l/ 13
crimson /ˈkrɪmz(ə)n/ 16
crisp /krɪsp/ 33
crop /krɒp/ 9
cross /krɒs/ 10
crowded /ˈkraʊdɪd/ 10, 14
crowds /kraʊdz/ 2, 8, 27
cruel /ˈkruːəl/ 23
cultural /ˈkʌltʃərəl/ 34
currency /ˈkʌrənsɪ/ 12
curse /kɜːs/ 40
curtains /ˈkɜːtənz/ 29
customer /ˈkʌstəm(r)/ 10
customs /ˈkʌstəmz/ 27
cut /kʌt/ 26, 29
cynical /ˈsɪnɪk(ə)l/ 23

daily /ˈdeɪlɪ/ 24
damage /ˈdæmɪdʒ/ 34
dance /dɑːns/ 27
danger /ˈdeɪndʒə(r)/ 27
dangerous /ˈdeɪndʒərəs/ 14
dashboard /ˈdæʃbɔːd/ 32
dazed /deɪzd/ 25
death /deθ/ 35
deceitful /dɪˈsiːtfʊl/ 20
decorator /ˈdekəˌreɪtə(r)/ 29
defeat /dɪˈfiːt/ 12
delay /dɪˈleɪ/ 2, 27
deliberate /dɪˈlɪbərət/ 35
delighted /dɪˈlaɪtɪd/ PC 6-10
delightful /dɪˈlaɪtfʊl/ 21
demonstration
   /ˌdemənˈstreɪʃ(ə)n/ 12
denim /ˈdenɪm/ 16
departures /dɪˈpɑːtʃə(r)/ 2
depend on /dɪˈpend ɒn/ 17
depressing /dɪˈpresɪŋ/ 5
design /dɪˈzaɪn/ 28
designer /dɪˈzaɪnə(r)/ 18
desk /desk/ 25
diamond /ˈdaɪəmənd/ 15
diary /ˈdaɪərɪ/ 31
direct /daɪˈrekt/ 20, 23
dirty /ˈdɜːtɪ/ 14, 29
disappear /ˌdɪsəˈpɪə(r)/ 17, 35, 38
disaster /dɪˈzɑːstə(r)/ 38
dish /dɪʃ/ 26, 33, 37
dishwasher /ˈdɪʃˌwɒʃə(r)/ 29
distribution /ˌdɪstrɪˈbjuːʃ(ə)n/ 24
district /ˈdɪstrɪkt/ 14
diving /ˈdaɪvɪŋ/ 27
divorced /dɪˈvɔːst/ 1
do /duː/ 1
do away with
   /duː əˈweɪ wɪθ/ PC 21-25
do something behind someone's
   back /duː ˈsʌmθɪŋ bɪˈhaɪnd
   ˈsʌmwʌnz bæk/ 36
do-it-yourself (DIY)
   /duː ɪt jɔːˈself/ 1
documentary /ˌdɒkjʊˈmentrɪ/ 24
draught /drɑːft/ 17
dreadful /ˈdredfʊl/ 4
drink /drɪŋk/ 1, 9
dripping /ˈdrɪpɪŋ/ 29
drop off /drɒp ɒf/ PC 21-25
drown /draʊn/ 35
drugstore /ˈdrʌgstɔː(r)/ 40
dull /dʌl/ 4
dusk /dʌsk/ 25
dusty /ˈdʌstɪ/ 29

eagle /ˈiːg(ə)l/ 22
earrings /ˈɪərɪŋz/ 16
easy-going /ˌiːzɪˈgəʊɪŋ/ 20
economic /ˌiːkəˈnɒmɪk/ 34
economics /ˌiːkəˈnɒmɪks/ 39
edition /ɪˈdɪʃ(ə)n/ 24
editor /ˈedɪtə(r)/ 24
election /ɪˈlekʃ(ə)n/ 12
electrician /ˌɪlekˈtrɪʃ(ə)n/ 29
electricity /ˌɪlekˈtrɪsɪtɪ/ 28
elementary school
   /ˌelɪˈmentərɪ skuːl/ 39
elephant /ˈelɪfənt/ 22
elevator /ˈelɪˌveɪtə(r)/ 40
embarrass /ɪmˈbærəs/ 34
emotional /ɪˈməʊʃən(ə)l/ 21
enamel /ɪˈnæm(ə)l/ 25
enemy /ˈenəmɪ/ 13
energy /ˈenədʒɪ/ 34
engagement /ɪnˈgeɪdʒmənt/ 3
engagement ring
   /ɪnˈgeɪdʒmənt rɪŋ/ 15
engine /ˈendʒɪn/ 32
entertaining /ˌentəˈteɪnɪŋ/ 4
environmental
   /ɪnˌvaɪrənˈment(ə)l/ 34
equator /ɪˈkweɪtə(r)/ 35
exciting /ɪkˈsaɪtɪŋ/ 4, 5
exercise /ˈeksəˌsaɪz/ 1
exhaust /ɪgˈzɔːst/ 32, 35
explain /ɪkˈspleɪn/ 1
explore /ɪkˈsplɔː(r)/ 38
extraordinary /ɪkˈstrɔːdɪnərɪ/ 21

face /feɪs/ 38
face up to /feɪs ʌp tʊ/ PC 21-25
factory /ˈfæktərɪ/ 28
faded /ˈfeɪdɪd/ 29
faint /feɪnt/ 25
fair /feə(r)/ 20
fair-minded /feə(r) maɪndɪd/ 20
faithful /ˈfeɪθfʊl/ 23
faithfulness /ˈfeɪθfʊlnes/ 6
falcon /ˈfɔːlkən/ 22
fall back on /fɔːl bæk ɒn/ PC 21-25
fall in love with someone
   /fɔːl ɪn lʌv wɪθ ˈsʌmwʌn/ 36
fall out with someone /fɔːl aʊt wɪθ
   ˈsʌmwʌn/ 36
fall through /fɔːl θruː/ PC 21-25
family /ˈfæməlɪ/ 7
fancy someone /ˈfænsɪ ˈsʌmwʌn/ 36
fantastic /fænˈtæstɪk/ 21
far-fetched /fɑː(r) fetʃət/ 21
fare /feə(r)/ 2
farmer /ˈfɑːmə(r)/ 18
fascinating /ˈfæsɪˌneɪtɪŋ/ PC 6-10
fashionable /ˈfæʃnəb(ə)l/ 18
father /ˈfɑːðə(r)/ 1
fatigue /fəˈtiːg/ 17
favourite /ˈfeɪvrɪt/ 1
feel jealous /fiːl ˈdʒeləs/ 36
fellow /ˈfeləʊ/ 40
feminism /ˈfemɪˌnɪz(ə)m/ 35
ferry /ˈferɪ/ 27
fiancé(e) /fɪˈɒnseɪ/ 36
fictional /ˈfɪkʃ(ə)nəl/ 13
field /fiːld/ 28, 30
fight /faɪt/ 30
fire /faɪə(r)/ 12
first name /fɜːst naɪm/ 1
fishing /ˈfɪʃɪŋ/ 4
fit /fɪt/ 18
fix /fɪks/ 29
flamboyant /flæmˈbɔɪənt/ 18
flares /fleə(r)z/ 16
flat /flæt/ 1, 17
flicker /ˈflɪkə(r)/ 40
flip-flops /ˈflɪp flɒps/ 16
floor /flɔː(r)/ 38
fly /flaɪ/ 33
folk /fəʊk/ 5
follow /ˈfɒləʊ/ 40
fond /fɒnd/ PC 11-15

food /fuːd/ 1, 8
foolish /ˈfuːlɪʃ/ 8
football /ˈfʊtbɔːl/ 4, 30
foreigner /ˈfɒrɪnə(r)/ 8
fork /fɔːk/ 26
fountain pen /ˈfaʊntɪn pen/ 15
frame /freɪm/ 15
freezing /ˈfriːzɪŋ/ 8, PC 6-10
friend /frend/ 8, 36
frightened /ˈfraɪt(ə)nd/ PC 11-15
frightening /ˈfraɪtənɪŋ/ 8
frog /frɒg/ 13
frown /fraʊn/ 40
fruit /fruːt/ 28
frustration /frʌˈstreɪʃən/ 35
fry /fraɪ/ 26
frying pan /ˈfraɪŋ pæn/ 26
fuel gauge /ˈfjuːəl geɪdʒ/ 32
fun /fʌn/ 4, 18
funk /fʌŋk/ 5
funny /ˈfʌnɪ/ 18, 21
fur hat /fɜː(r) hæt/ 8
furious /ˈfjʊərɪəs/ PC 6-10

gale /geɪl/ 12
game /geɪm/ 7, 30
garden /ˈgɑːd(ə)n/ 29
gardener /ˈgɑːdnə(r)/ 18, 29
gardening /ˈgɑːd(ə)nɪŋ/ 4
gate /geɪt/ 29
gear lever /gɪə(r) ˈliːvə(r)/ 32
generous /ˈdʒenərəs/ PC 11-15
geography /dʒɪˈɒgrəfɪ/ 39
get away /get əˈweɪ/ PC 21-25
get back /get bæk/ PC 21-25
get down /get daʊn/ PC 21-25
get engaged to someone
   /get ɪnˈgeɪdʒd tu ˈsʌmwʌn/ 36
get involved with someone
   /get ɪnˈvɒlvd wɪθ ˈsʌmwʌn/ 36
get married to someone
   /get ˈmærɪd tu ˈsʌmwʌn/ 36
get on with /get ɒn wɪθ/ PC 21-25
get to know someone
   /get tu nəʊ ˈsʌmwʌn/ 36
get up /get ʌp/ 1
giraffe /dʒɪˈrɑːf/ 22
girlfriend /ˈgɜːlfrend/ 36
give up /gɪv ʌp/ PC 21-25
glad /glæd/ PC 11-15
glass /glɑːs/ 15
go down with
   /gəʊ daʊn wɪθ/ PC 21-25
go in for /gəʊ ɪn fə(r)/ PC 21-25
go off /gəʊ ɒf/ PC 21-25
go out with /gəʊ aʊt wɪθ/ 36
go to bed /gəʊ tə bed/ 1
go to work /gəʊ tə wɜːk/ 1
goal /gəʊl/ 30
going to nightclubs
   /ˈgəʊɪŋ tə naɪtklʌbz/ 4
gold /gəʊld/ 3, 15, 28
good looks /gʊd lʊks/ 6
good-humoured
   /gʊd ˈhjuːmə(r)d/ 20
gorilla /gəˈrɪlə/ 22
grab /græb/ 40
grade /greɪd/ 39
grade school /greɪd skuːl/ 39
greasy /ˈgriːsɪ/ 9
great /greɪt/ 4, 5
green peppers /griːn ˈpepə(r)z/ 26
grill /grɪl/ 26
gripping /ˈgrɪpɪŋ/ 21
groom /gruːm/ 3
grow /grəʊ/ 9, 28
gun /gʌn/ 12

hairdresser /ˈheəˌdresə(r)/ 18
ham /hæm/ 26
hamburger /ˈhæmˌbɜːgə(r)/ 26
handbag /ˈhænbæg/ 16
handkerchief /ˈhæŋkətʃɪf/ 31
harbour /ˈhɑːbə(r)/ 37

hard-working /hɑːd wɜːkɪŋ/ 18, 20
have dinner /hæv ˈdɪnə(r)/ 1
have lunch /hæv lʌntʃ/ 1
headlight /hedlaɪt/ 32
healthy /helθɪ/ 9
hear /hɪə(r)/ 1
heart /hɑːt/ 23
heat /hiːt/ 26
heavy metal /hevɪ ˈmet(ə)l/ 5
heavy /hevɪ/ 15
help /help/ 11
henna /henə/ 3
herbs /hɜːbz/ 9
hero /hɪərəʊ/ 13
hiccups /hɪkʌps/ 33
high heels /haɪ hiːlz/ 16
high school /haɪ skuːl/ 39
hijack /haɪdʒæk/ 12
hilarious /hɪˈleərɪəs/ PC 6-10
hilly /hɪlɪ/ 14
Hindu /hɪnduː/ 3
history /hɪst(ə)rɪ/ 39
hitchhike /hɪtʃhaɪk/ 19
hold back /həʊld bæk/ PC 21-25
holiday /hɒlɪˌdeɪ/ 19
honest /ɒnɪst/ 20, 23
honesty /ɒnɪstɪ/ 6
honeymoon /hʌnɪˌmuːn/ 3
horoscope /hɒrəˌskəʊp/ 3
horrible /hɒrɪb(ə)l/ 21
horror film /hɒrə(r) fɪlm/ 21
horseback /hɔːsbæk/ 19
hospitable /hɒspɪtəb(ə)l/ 8, 34
hostage /hɒstɪdʒ/ 12
hostel /hɒst(ə)l/ 19
hot dog /hɒt dɒg/ 26
house /haʊs/ 1
humid /hjuːmɪd/ 37
hurt /hɜːt/ 10
husband /hʌzbənd/ 1

ice cube /aɪs kjuːb/ 33
idealism /aɪdɪəlɪz(ə)m/ 6
ill /ɪl/ PC 11-15
imaginative /ɪˈmædʒɪnətɪv/ 18
impressive /ɪmˈpresɪv/ 21
in love /ɪn lʌv/ PC 11-15
in pairs /ɪn peə(r)z/ 1
incense /ɪnsens/ 19
independent /ˌɪndɪˈpend(ə)nt/ 24
indicator /ɪndɪˌkeɪtə(r)/ 32
indifferent /ɪnˈdɪfrənt/ 35
industrial /ɪnˈdʌstrɪəl/ 14
informality /ɪnˌfɔːˈmælɪtɪ/ 6
information desk
  /ˌɪnfəˈmeɪʃ(ə)n desk/ 2
infuriating /ɪnˈfjʊərɪˌeɪtɪŋ/ PC 6-10
intelligence /ɪnˈtelɪdʒ(ə)ns/ 6
intelligent /ɪnˈtelɪdʒ(ə)nt/ 18
interesting /ɪntrəstɪŋ/ 5
invent /ɪnˈvent/ 28
invest in /ɪnˈvest ɪn/ 7
invite /ɪnˈvaɪt/ 7
iron /aɪən/ 28
irritating /ɪrɪteɪtɪŋ/ 5
island /aɪlənd/ 27

jack /dʒæk/ 32
jacket /dʒækɪt/ 16
jaguar /dʒægjʊə(r)/ 22
jazz /dʒæz/ 5
jealous /dʒeləs/ 23
jeans /dʒiːnz/ 16
jewel /dʒuːəl/ 3
join /dʒɔɪn/ 7
journalist /dʒɜːnəˌlɪst/ 18
judge /dʒʌdʒ/ 12
junior high school
  /dʒuːnɪə(r) haɪ skuːl/ 39
junk /dʒʌŋk/ 37
jury /dʒʊərɪ/ 12

keys /kiːz/ 31
khaki /kɑːkɪ/ 16
kidnap /kɪdnæp/ 12

kind /kaɪnd/ 18, PC 11-15
kindergarten /kɪndəˌgɑːt(ə)n/ 39
kindness /kaɪndnɪs/ 6
knife /naɪf/ 26
knock down /nɒk daʊn/ 17

lamp /læmp/ 15
landmark /lændmɑːk/ 8
lane /leɪn/ 14, 30
languages /læŋgwɪdʒɪz/ 39
laugh /lɑːf/ 13
law /lɔː/ 39
lawnmower /lɔːnməʊ(r)/ 29
lawyer /lɔɪə(r)/ 12
lay /leɪ/ 11
leather jacket /leðə(r) ˈdʒækɪt/ 16
leather /leðə(r)/ 16
leave /liːv/ 2
left wing /left wɪŋ/ 12, 24
left-handed /left ˈhændɪd/ 20
leopard /lepəd/ 22
lettuce /letɪs/ 33
liberal /lɪbər(ə)l/ 24
lid /lɪd/ 33
lie /laɪ/ 11
lie about something
  /laɪ əˈbaʊt ˈsʌmθɪŋ/ 36
lifestyle /laɪfstaɪl/ 34
light /laɪt/ 29
lightning /laɪtnɪŋ/ 12
likely /laɪklɪ/ PC 11-15
limp /lɪmp/ 33
linen /lɪnɪn/ 16
lion /laɪən/ 22
liquid /lɪkwɪd/ 9
listen to /lɪst(ə)n tə/ 1
live /lɪv/ 1
lively /laɪvlɪ/ 14, 18
lobby /lɒbɪ/ 37
local /ləʊk(ə)l/ 34
lock /lɒk/ 38
lonely /ləʊnlɪ/ 8
look out /lʊk aʊt/ PC 21-25
look up /lʊk ʌp/ 1
lose /luːz/ 12
lose your way /luːz jɔː(r) weɪ/ 27
lost /lɒst/ 27
love story /lʌv stɔːrɪ/ 21
luggage /lʌgɪdʒ/ 2
lump /lʌmp/ 33

magazine /ˌmægəˈziːn/ 24
make /meɪk/ 1, 28
make up for
  /meɪk ʌp fɔː(r)/ PC 21-25
male-dominated
  /meɪl ˈdɒmɪˌneɪtɪd/ 35
manhole /mænhəʊl/ 38
manufacture /ˌmænjʊˈfæktʃə(r)/ 28
map /mæp/ 8, 31
march /mɑːtʃ/ 12
mark /mɑːk/ 33
market /mɑːkɪt/ 14
marriage /mærɪdʒ/ 3
married /mærɪd/ 1
match /mætʃ/ 1, 12, 30
matchmaker /mætʃmeɪkə(r)/ 3
maths /mæθs/ 39
meal /miːl/ 10
mean /miːn/ 10
meaning /miːnɪŋ/ 1
medicine /medsən/ 39
meet someone /miːt sʌmwʌn/ 36
meeting /miːtɪŋ/ 40
memories /memərɪz/ 7
mend /mend/ 11, 29
metal /met(ə)l/ 15
middle-aged /mɪdl eɪdʒd/ 20
middle-of-the-road
  /mɪdl əv ðə rəʊd/ 5
middle school /mɪdl skuːl/ 39
milk /mɪlk/ 9
mine /maɪn/ 28
miniskirt /mɪnɪˌskɜːt/ 37
mirror /mɪrə(r)/ 31, 32

missile /mɪsaɪl/ 12
mistake /mɪsteɪk/ 1
mix /mɪks/ 26
moan /məʊn/ 38
mobile phone /məʊbaɪl fəʊn/ 31
mocking /mɒkɪŋ/ 17
model /mɒd(ə)l/ 17
money /mʌnɪ/ 7
moon /muːn/ 23
moose /muːs/ 22
mop up /mɒp ʌp/ 33
Moslem /mɒzlɪm/ 3
mother /mʌðə(r)/ 1
mountain /maʊntɪn/ 27
moustache /məsˈtɑːʃ/ 16
movie /muːvɪ/ 13
moving /muːvɪŋ/ 5
mugging /mʌgɪŋ/ 27
murder /mɜːdə(r)/ 40
museum /mjuːˈzɪəm/ 14
music /mjuːzɪk/ 39
musical /mjuːzɪkl/ 21
mussels /mʌs(ə)lz/ 26
mysterious /mɪsˈtɪərɪəs/ 40
mysteriously /mɪsˈtɪərɪəslɪ/ 38
mystery /mɪstərɪ/ 35

national /næʃ(ə)n(ə)l/ 24
nationality /ˌnæʃəˈnælɪtɪ/ 1
navy /neɪvɪ/ 12, 16
necklace /nekləs/ 15
neighbourhood /neɪbəˌhʊd/ 40
neighbours /neɪbə(r)z/ 7
newspaper /njuːzˌpeɪpə(r)/ 24
nice /naɪs/ 4
noisy /nɔɪzɪ/ 14
noon /nuːn/ 40
not working /nɒt wɜːkɪŋ/ 29
notebook /nəʊtbʊk/ 31
notes /nəʊtz/ 1
number /nʌmbə(r)/ 1
number plate /nʌmbə(r) pleɪt/ 32
numerous /njuːmərəs/ 35
nurse /nɜːs/ 18

oblivious /əˈblɪvɪəs/ 40
obscure /əbˈskjʊə(r)/ 35
officer /ɒfɪsə(r)/ 12
oil /ɔɪl/ 26
OK /əʊˈkeɪ/ 4
old /əʊld/ 1
old-fashioned /əʊldˈfæʃnd/ 14, 20, 29
olive /ɒlɪv/ 16
olive oil /ɒlɪv ɔɪl/ 33
one-way /wʌn weɪ/ 2
onion /ʌnɪən/ 23, 26
open /əʊpən/ 20
openness /əʊpənəs/ 6
opera /ɒprə/ 5
optimism /ɒptəˈmɪz(ə)m/ 6
organised /ɔːgənaɪzd/ 18
outgoing /aʊtˌgəʊɪŋ/ 20
outspoken /aʊtspəʊkən/ 20
oven /ʌv(ə)n/ 26, 29, 33
overflowing /əʊvəˈfləʊɪŋ/ 29
overgrown /əʊvəˈgrəʊn/ 29
oysters /ɔːstə(r)z/ 26

package tour /pækɪdʒ tʊər/ 19
paint /peɪnt/ 29
painting /peɪntɪŋ/ 4, 15
palace /pælɪs/ 14
panda /pændə/ 22
paper /peɪpə(r)/ 15
paperback novel
  /peɪpə(r) bæk nɒv(ə)l/ 31
paragraph /pærəˌgrɑːf/ 1
park /pɑːk/ 14
park keeper /pɑːk ˈkiːpə(r)/ 18
partner /pɑːtnə(r)/ 36
party /pɑːtɪ/ 12
passage /pæsɪdʒ/ 1
passenger /pæsɪndʒə(r)/ 2
passionate /pæʃənət/ 5, 23
pasta /pæstə/ 26

paste /peɪst/ 3
pasty /pæstɪ/ 8
patience /peɪʃ(ə)ns/ 6
pay attention /peɪ əˈtenʃ(ə)n/ 38
peace /piːs/ 27
peak season /piːk ˈsiːz(ə)n/ 37
pearls /pɜːlz/ 25
pedal /ped(ə)l/ 32
peel /piːl/ 26
peeling /piːlɪŋ/ 29
penknife /pen naɪf/ 31
pepper /pepə(r)/ 9, 26
pet /pet/ 13
philosophy /frlɒsəfɪ/ 39
photo /fəʊtəʊ/ 15, 34
phrase /freɪz/ 1
physical education
  /fɪzɪkl ˌedjʊˈkeɪʃ(ə)n/ 39
physics /fɪzɪks/ 39
pick up /pɪk ʌp/ 11
picnic /pɪknɪk/ 40
picnic basket /pɪknɪk bæskɪt/ 15
picture /pɪktʃə(r)/ 17
picturesque /ˌpɪktʃəˈresk/ 14
pie /paɪ/ 26
pigeon /pɪdʒɪn/ 22
pilgrim /pɪlgrɪm/ 19
pizza /piːtsə/ 26
plague /pleɪg/ 38
plain /pleɪn/ 9
plastic /plæstɪk/ 15
plate /pleɪt/ 26
play /pleɪ/ 7, 30
player /pleɪə(r)/ 12, 30
playground /pleɪgraʊnd/ 8
playing cards /pleɪɪŋ kɑːds/ 4
pleased /pliːzd/ PC 11-15
plumber /plʌmə(r)/ 29
pocket knife /pɒkɪt naɪf/ 17
police officer /pəˈliːs ˈɒfɪsə(r)/ 18
polish /pɒlɪʃ/ 33
political /pəˈlɪtɪk(ə)l/ 24
pollution /pəˈluːʃ(ə)n/ 34
ponytail /pəʊnɪteɪl/ 16
pool /puːl/ 30
pop /pɒp/ 5
popular /pɒpjʊlə(r)/ 13, 24, 34
porcelain /pɔːsəlɪn/ 15, 37
possessive /pəˈzesɪv/ 23
postcard /pəʊstkɑːd/ 27
pottery /pɒtərɪ/ 28
pour /pɔː(r)/ 26
power station
  /paʊə(r) ˈsteɪʃ(ə)n/ 28
powerful /paʊəfʊl/ 21
practical /præktɪk(ə)l/ 18
prejudiced /predʒʊdɪst/ 20
present /prez(ə)nt/ 10
president /prezɪdənt/ 12
pretty /prɪtɪ/ 25
prices /praɪsɪz/ 1
priest /priːst/ 3, 19
primary school /praɪmərɪ skuːl/ 39
prime minister
  /praɪm ˈmɪnɪstə(r)/ 12
privacy /prɪvəsɪ/ 35
produce /prəˈdjuːs/ 9, 28
programme /prəʊgræm/ 24
programmes /prəʊgræmz/ 7
prominent /prɒmɪnənt/ 35
promise /prɒmɪs/ 3
pronounce /prəˈnaʊns/ 1
propaganda /ˌprɒpəˈgændə/ 35
propose /prəˈpəʊz/ 3
protection /prəˈtekʃ(ə)n/ 35
proud /praʊd/ PC 11-15
prove /pruːv/ 25
public /pʌblɪk/ 34
public school /pʌblɪk skuːl/ 39
publish /pʌblɪʃ/ 24
puppy /pʌpɪ/ 33
puzzled /pʌz(ə)ld/ 40

quality /kwɒlɪtɪ/ 24
quay /kiː/ 14

question /ˈkwestʃ(ə)n/ 1
quiz show /kwɪz ʃəʊ/ 24
rabbit /ˈræbɪt/ 13
race /reɪs/ 30
racket /ˈrækɪt/ 30
radio /ˈreɪdɪəʊ/ 32
rag /ræg/ 33
rain /reɪn/ 12
rap /ræp/ 5
read /riːd/ 1
reader /ˈriːdə(r)/ 24
readership /ˈriːdə(r)ʃɪp/ 24
reading /ˈriːdɪŋ/ 4, 39
ready /ˈredɪ/ PC 11-15
rear light /rɪə(r) laɪt/ 32
reception /rɪˈsepʃ(ə)n/ 3
receptionist /rɪˈsepʃ(ə)nɪst/ 18
record /ˈrekɔːd/ 35
rectangular /rekˈtæŋɡʊlə(r)/ 15
referee /refəˈriː/ 30
reggae /ˈreɡeɪ/ 5
regional /ˈriːdʒən(ə)l/ 24
registry office /ˈredʒɪstrɪ ˈɒfɪs/ 3
related /rɪˈleɪtɪd/ PC 11-15
relax /rɪˈlæks/ 37
relaxing /rɪˈlæksɪŋ/ 4, 5
reliability /rɪˌlaɪəˈbɪlɪtɪ/ 6
reliable /rɪˈlaɪəb(ə)l/ 18
relieved /rɪˈliːvd/ 8
remarkable /rɪˈmɑːkəb(ə)l/ 21
remove /rɪˈmuːv/ 33
repair /rɪˈpeə(r)/ 29
repeat /rɪˈpiːt/ 1
replace /rɪˈpleɪs/ 29
replaster /riːˈplɑːstə(r)/ 29
reservation /ˌrezəˈveɪʃn/ 2
reserved /rɪˈzɜːvd/ 20
retire /rɪˈtaɪə(r)/ 35
rhinoceros /raɪˈnɒsərəs/ 22
rice /raɪs/ 28
ridiculous /rɪˈdɪkjʊləs/ PC 6-10
right wing /raɪt wɪŋ/ 12, 24
ring /rɪŋ/ 3, 23, 30
river /ˈrɪvə(r)/ 14, 27
roast /rəʊst/ 26
rock /rɒk/ 5
romantic /rəʊˈmæntɪk/ 14
roof /ruːf/ 32
rose /rəʊz/ 23
round /raʊnd/ 15
round trip /raʊnd trɪp/ 2
round-the- world
    /raʊnd ðə wɜːld/ 35
rubber /ˈrʌbə(r)/ 15
rumour /ˈruːmə(r)/ 35
run /rʌn/ 30
run away with
    /rʌn əˈweɪ wɪθ/ PC 21-25
running /ˈrʌnɪŋ/ 4

sad /sæd/ 5
sail /seɪl/ 27
sailor /ˈseɪlə(r)/ 18
saint /seɪnt/ 19
salsa /ˈsælsə/ 5
salt /sɔːlt/ 26
sandals /ˈsænd(ə)lz/ 16, 37
sarcastic /sɑːˈkæstɪk/ 23
sari /ˈsɑːriː/ 3
satellite /ˈsætəˌlaɪt/ 24
sauce /sɔːs/ 9
saucepan /ˈsɔːspən/ 26
sausage /ˈsɒsɪdʒ/ 8
savoury /ˈseɪvərɪ/ 9
say /seɪ/ 1
scarlet /ˈskɑːlət/ 16
scent /sent/ 25
science and technology
    /ˈsaɪəns ənd tekˈnɒlədʒɪ/ 39
science-fiction film
    /ˈsaɪəns ˈfɪkʃ(ə)n fɪlm/ 21
score /skɔː(r)/ 30
scrape off /skreɪp ɒf/ 33
scratched /skrætʃt/ 29
screen /skriːn/ 17

seafood /ˈsiːfuːd/ 26
seal /siːl/ 38
seat belt /siːt belt/ 32
secondary school
    /ˈsekəndrɪ skuːl/ 39
secretary /ˈsekrətrɪ/ 18
self-assured /self əˈʃʊəd/ 20
send off /send ɒf/ 30
sensible /ˈsensəb(ə)l/ 18
sensitive /ˈsensətɪv/ 18, 20, 21
sentence /ˈsent(ə)ns/ 1
series /ˈsɪəriːz/ 13
serious /ˈsɪərɪəs/ 20
seriousness /ˈsɪərɪəsnəs/ 6
servant /ˈsɜːv(ə)nt/ 25
serve /sɜːv/ 30
shell /ʃel/ 19
shine /ʃaɪn/ 33
shiny /ˈʃaɪnɪ/ 33
ships /ʃɪps/ 28
shopping /ˈʃɒpɪŋ/ 4
shopping mall /ˈʃɒpɪŋ mæl/ 37
short-sighted /ʃɔːt saɪtɪd/ 20
short-tempered /ʃɔːt ˈtempəd/ 20
shorts /ʃɔːts/ 37
show /ʃəʊ/ 24
shower /ˈʃaʊə(r)/ 29
shutters /ˈʃʌtə(r)z/ 29
shy /ʃaɪ/ 5
sidelight /ˈsaɪdlaɪt/ 32
side street /saɪd striːt/ 38
sights /saɪts/ 34
sightseeing /ˈsaɪtsiːɪŋ/ 19
silk /sɪlk/ 16, 37
silly /ˈsɪlɪ/ 5
similar /ˈsɪmələ(r)/ PC 11-15
simple /ˈsɪmp(ə)l/ 21
sincerity /sɪnˈserɪtɪ/ 6
single /ˈsɪŋɡl/ 1
single-mindedness
    /ˈsɪŋɡl maɪndɪdnəs/ 6
sink /sɪŋk/ 29
sip /sɪp/ 33
sister /ˈsɪstə(r)/ 1
sitcom /ˈsɪtkɒm/ 24
sitting /ˈsɪtɪŋ/ 17
skiing /ˈskiːŋ/ 30
skill /skɪl/ 40
skyscraper /ˈskaɪˌskreɪpə(r)/ 14
sleepy /ˈsliːpɪ/ 14
slice /slaɪs/ 26
slope /sləʊp/ 30
slow /sləʊ/ 21
smart /smɑːt/ 14, 18
smile /smaɪl/ 8, 25
snake /sneɪk/ 23
snow /snəʊ/ 8, 27
soap opera /ˈsəʊp ˈɒpərə/ 24
sociable /ˈsəʊʃəb(ə)l/ 18
sofa /ˈsəʊfə/ 15, 29
soft-hearted /sɒft hɑːtɪd/ 20
softness /ˈsɒftnəs/ 25
soldier /ˈsəʊldʒə(r)/ 8, 12, 18
solid /ˈsɒlɪd/ 9
solo /ˈsəʊləʊ/ 35
sorry /ˈsɒrɪ/ PC 11-15
soul /səʊl/ 35
souvenirs /ˌsuːvəˈnɪə(r)z/ 19
spanner /ˈspænə(r)/ 23
spare time /speə(r) taɪm/ 1
spectacular
    /spekˈtækjʊlə(r)/ 21, 37
speculate /ˈspekjʊˌleɪt/ 35
speed limit /spiːd lɪmɪt/ 27
speedometer /spiːˈdɒmɪtə(r)/ 32
spell /spel/ 1
spend /spend/ 7
spices /spaɪsɪz/ 9
spoon /spuːn/ 26
sport /spɔːt/ 1
spot /spɒt/ 33
spread /spred/ 26, 33
spy /spaɪ/ 13
square /skweə(r)/ 14, 15
stadium /ˈsteɪdɪəm/ 12

stain /steɪn/ 33
stained /steɪnd/ 29
stairs /steə(r)z/ 29
stale /steɪl/ 8
stamp /stæmp/ 19
stand back /stænd bæk/ PC 21-25
stand up to /stænd ʌp tə/ PC 21-25
startled /ˈstɑːt(ə)ld/ 25
statement /ˈsteɪtmənt/ 1
station /ˈsteɪʃ(ə)n/ 24
statue /ˈstætjuː/ 19
steam /stiːm/ 37
steel /stiːl/ 29
steering wheel /stɪə(r)ɪŋ wiːl/ 32
stone /stəʊn/ 16
stove /stəʊv/ 17
strained /streɪnd/ 35
stranger /ˈstreɪndʒə(r)/ 8
strawberry /ˈstrɔːbərɪ/ 23
street /striːt/ 14
stretch /stretʃ/ 33
strong-willed /strɒŋ wɪld/ 20
stubble /ˈstʌb(ə)l/ 16
stuck /stʌk/ 29
studio /ˈstjuːdɪəʊ/ 17
success /səkˈses/ 13
sugar /ˈʃʊɡə(r)/ 9
suitcase /ˈsuːtkeɪs/ 2
summer /ˈsʌmə(r)/ 37
sunbathe /ˈsʌnbeɪð/ 27
sunburn /ˈsʌnbɜːn/ 27
sunglasses /ˈsʌnɡlɑːsɪz/ 16
superb /suːˈpɜːb/ 4
sure /ʃʊə(r)/ PC 11-15
surname /ˈsɜːneɪm/ 1
survive /səˈvaɪv/ 35
sweet /swiːt/ 4
swimming /ˈswɪmɪŋ/ 4, 30
swimming pool /ˈswɪmɪŋ puːl/ 27

T-shirt /tiː ʃɜːt/ 16
table /ˈteɪbl/ 1
tabloid /ˈtæblɔɪd/ 24
tactful /ˈtæktfʊl/ 20
take out /teɪk aʊt/ 11
talent /ˈtælənt/ 1
Taoist /ˈtaʊɪst/ 3
tap /tæp/ 29
tea /tiː/ 28
teacher /ˈtiːtʃə(r)/ 18
team /tiːm/ 12, 13
tears /tɪə(r)z/ 25
techno /ˈteknəʊ/ 5
temptation /tempˈteɪʃ(ə)n/ 19
tennis /ˈtenɪs/ 4, 30
terrible /ˈterɪb(ə)l/ 4, 21
terrific /təˈrɪfɪk/ 4
terrifying /ˈterɪˌfaɪɪŋ/ PC 6-10
terrorist /ˈterərɪst/ 12
theatre /ˈθɪətə(r)/ 14
thick-skinned /θɪk skɪnd/ 20
threaten /ˈθret(ə)n/ 40
thriller /ˈθrɪlə(r)/ 21
thrilling /ˈθrɪlɪŋ/ 5
throw away /θrəʊ əˈweɪ/ 11
thunderstorm /ˈθʌndəˌstɔːm/ 12, 27
tick /tɪk/ 1
ticket /ˈtɪkɪt/ 2
tickets /ˈtɪkɪts/ 7
tidy /ˈtaɪdɪ/ 11
tie /taɪ/ 33
tiger /ˈtaɪɡə(r)/ 22
tight /taɪt/ 33
tiles /taɪlz/ 38
timetable /ˈtaɪmteɪbl/ 2
tobacco /təˈbækəʊ/ 17, 28
toilet /ˈtɔɪlət/ 29
torch /tɔːtʃ/ 15
torn /tɔːn/ 29
tortoise /ˈtɔːtəs/ 22
towelling /ˈtaʊəlɪŋ/ 16
town hall /taʊn hɔːl/ 3
tracks /træks/ 40
traffic /ˈtræfɪk/ 24
train spotting /treɪn spɒtɪŋ/ 4

tram /træm/ 14
transport /trænsˈpɔːt/ 34
troops /truːps/ 12
turkey /ˈtɜːkɪ/ 26
turn back /tɜːn bæk/ PC 21-25
turn on /tɜːn ɒn/ 11
turquoise /ˈtɜːkwɔɪz/ 16
typical /ˈtɪpɪk(ə)l/ 13, PC 11-15
typing /ˈtaɪpɪŋ/ 39

umbrella /ʌmˈbrelə/ 31
unable /ʌnˈeɪb(ə)l/ PC 11-15
underline /ˈʌndəlaɪn/ 1
unemotional /ˌʌnɪˈməʊʃən(ə)l/ 20
unfaithful /ʌnˈfeɪθfʊl/ 23
unique /juːˈniːk/ 14

vase /vɑːz/ 15
veil /veɪl/ 3
vest /vest/ 16
vet /vet/ 18
victory /ˈvɪktərɪ/ 12
video /ˈvɪdɪəʊ/ 24
view /vjuː/ 37
viewer /ˈvjuː(r)/ 24
violin /ˌvaɪəˈlɪn/ 15
visa /ˈviːzə/ 27
vulture /ˈvʌltʃə(r)/ 22

waistcoat /ˈweɪstkəʊt/ 16
waiter /ˈweɪtə(r)/ 10
waitress /ˈweɪtrəs/ 18
walker /ˈwɔːkə(r)/ 19
walking /ˈwɔːkɪŋ/ 4
wall /wɔːl/ 29
wallet /ˈwɒlɪt/ 10
wallpaper /ˈwɔːlˌpeɪpə(r)/ 29
war /wɔː(r)/ 12, 13
warm /wɔːm/ 9
warmth /wɔːmθ/ 25
wash /wɒʃ/ 29
waste /weɪst/ 7
wealthy /ˈwelθɪ/ 14
weapon /ˈwepən/ 12
wear off /weə(r) ɒf/ PC 21-25
weekly /ˌwiːklɪ/ 24
well /wel/ PC 11-15
well-behaved /wel bɪˈheɪvd/ 20
well-dressed /wel drest/ 25
western /ˈwest(ə)n/ 21
wet /wet/ 33
whale /weɪl/ 22
wheat /wiːt/ 28
wheel /wiːl/ 32
whistle /ˈwɪs(ə)l/ 40
wife /waɪf/ 1
win /wɪn/ 12
wind /wɪnd/ 8
window pane /ˈwɪndəʊ peɪn/ 29
windscreen /ˈwɪndskriːn/ 32
wine /waɪn/ 28
wing /wɪŋ/ 32
wipers /ˈwaɪpə(r)z/ 32
wiring /ˈwaɪərɪŋ/ 29
witness /ˈwɪtnɪs/ 3
wonderful /ˈwʌndəˌfʊl/ 4
wood /wʊd/ 15
wool /wʊl/ 15, 16, 28
word /wɜːd/ 1
work /wɜːk/ 1
workshop /ˈwɜːk ʃɒp/ 28
world-famous /wɜːld ˈfeɪməs/ 20
worn /wɔːn/ 29
wrap /ræp/ 33
wrap up /ræp ʌp/ 11
wreck /rek/ 27
wristwatch /rɪst wɒtʃ/ 15
write /raɪt/ 1, 7
writing /ˈraɪtɪŋ/ 39

yard /jɑːd/ 28
young /jʌŋ/ 18
youngster /ˈjʌŋstə(r)/ 38

zebra /ˈzebrə/ 22

Wordbank

Use the categories below to help you organise new vocabulary.
Try and write each new word in at least two different categories.
You may also like to write down words which often go with the
new vocabulary items.

character	clothes	countries and nationalities
crime and justice	customs and traditions	daily life
days, months, seasons	education	environmental issues
family and friends	food and drink	geographical features and locations
health and physical feelings	house and home	language learning
leisure interests	the media	parts of the body
personal information	personal possessions	physical appearance
politics, government and society	religion	shops and shopping
social situations	town features and facilities	transport
travel	work	weather

Heinemann English Language Teaching
A division of Reed Educational
and Professional Publishing Limited
Halley Court, Jordan Hill, Oxford OX2 8EJ

OXFORD MADRID FLORENCE ATHENS PRAGUE SÃO PAULO
MEXICO CITY CHICAGO PORTSMOUTH (NH) TOKYO SINGAPORE
KUALA LUMPUR MELBOURNE AUCKLAND JOHANNESBURG
IBADAN GABORONE

ISBN 0 435 24025 0

© Diana Pye, Simon Greenall 1995
Design and illustration © Heinemann Publishers
(Oxford) Ltd 1995

First published 1995

Designed by Stafford & Stafford

Cover design by Stafford & Stafford

Illustrations by
Frances Lloyd, pp2, 4, 22, 47
Ed McLachlan, pp12, 19, 40, 41, 51, 61
Martin Sanders, pp9, 15, 17, 25, 31, 34, 35, 36,
    45, 56, 58, 66, 67, 77, 81

Acknowledgements

The authors and publishers would like to thank the
following for their kind permission to reproduce material
in this book:

Sue Blackhall for the extract taken from *The World's
Greatest Blunders* by Octopus Books; Madelyn Burley-
Allen for the extract from *Memory Skills in Business*,
reproduced by permission of Kogan Page Ltd; Edna
Corran for the extract *The Corridor*; *The European* for the
articles 'Chocolate Boutique in Paris' by Margret Kemp,
'Icy Sun on St Petersburg' 21–7/1/94, 'The Night Express'
by Slawomir Mrozek and 'Some Rattlin' Good Recipes'
20–6/5/94; Stephen Fellows for the extract taken from
Reflections; *The Independent* for the article 'Kiwi waddles
amiably towards extinction' by Nicholas Schoon, IOS
19/6/94; *Le Courrier de l'UNESCO* for the extracts from the
article 'The Night of the Henna' by Mahmoud Hussein,
Sept 89, and 'A National Obsession' by Samir Gharib, Oct
92; *The Observer* for an extract from the article 'The Dead
of Night' by Dr John Collie, 13/3/94; *The Telegraph* for
the article 'A Mini Saga', reproduced by permission of
Ewan MacNaughton Associates; *The Times* for the articles
'Traffic Cones', Sunday Times 17/4/94, 'American Eagle
soars out of Danger's Reach' by Ben Macintyre 30/6/94;
Wexas Ltd for the extract 'The Adventure Traveller' by
Paul Vickers taken from *The Traveller's Handbook*,
revised 1991.

Photographs by: Jonathan Eastland/Ajax News and
Feature Service p24; Stuart Clarke/Impact Photos p75;
Alan Keohane/Impact Photos p28; Tony Stone Images
pp10, 37, 68, 75; The Telegraph Colour Library p24; Trip
pp3, 28.

While every effort has been made to trace the owners of
copyright material in this book, there have been some
cases when the publishers have been unable to contact
the owners. We should be grateful to hear from anyone
who recognises their copyright material and who is
unacknowledged. We shall be pleased to make the
necessary amendments in future editions of the book.

Printed and bound in Great Britain by Thomson Litho Ltd,
East Kilbride, Glasgow

96 97 98 99 10 9 8 7 6 5 4 3 2